'Jemma, Jemma,' he said against her hair, 'do you know what you do to a man?'

She whispered, forehead against the smooth fabric of his shirt, 'Maybe I do, maybe I don't. You can tell me if you like.'

The laugh he gave rumbled under his ribs. 'In what capacity will you be listening? As Miss Hale the counsellor, dispassionate and cool, or as Jemma, the girl with warmth and laughter in her eyes and a mouth that says "kiss me if you can"?'

'I think,' with a firm smile, she eased away, 'I must put a distance between us for the moment.' He made as if to pull her back but changed his mind. 'You invited me here to talk to me, to tell me your problems. If I——' She ran her tongue around her lips. 'If I arouse your desires, activate your male reflexes, well, I'm sorry about that, but——'

'Don't be.'

THE BITTER TASTE OF LOVE

BY

LILIAN PEAKE

MILLS & BOON LIMITED
ETON HOUSE   18-24 PARADISE ROAD
RICHMOND   SURREY   TW9 1SR

First published in Great Britain 1988 by Mills & Boon Limited

© Lilian Peake 1988

Australian copyright 1988 Philippine copyright 1988 This edition 1988

ISBN 0 263 76052 9

Set in Times Roman 10 on 12 pt. 01-0888-53531 C

Made and printed in Great Britain

CHAPTER ONE

CINDY swept through the door from her own office and into Jemma's. 'The man they call "the wanderer" is back,' she announced brightly. 'I've just seen him with my own eyes.' She paused for effect. 'And is he something!'

Jemma raised her head from the file she had been studying and shifted her brain into neutral. 'Back from what? And who's "he"?'

Cindy frowned. 'I forget his name, but he's one of the firm's directors. Rumour says——'

'You mean the man called Arne Drummond? He left the company before I joined.' She leaned back, massaging her neck muscles. 'What does rumour say?'

'That he didn't leave, but lost himself abroad for a couple of years. Middle East? Far East?' Cindy made a face. 'Geography never was my strong subject.'

Jemma smiled. The action was a relaxation in itself. Other people's problems were her job and these, as she had discovered in the past year, were truly no laughing matter. But that was the work she had been trained for and she loved it. So she wasn't grumbling.

'There was even a name mentioned,' her secretary added. 'Johanna. With an "h". That's all I know.'

Jemma nodded. The only Johanna with an 'h' that she knew was the wife of Dave Forrest, another director of the company.

'You've heard the story then?' Cindy asked, eager to be enlightened there and then.

Jemma had heard, but like so many other stories that came her way in the course of her work, she kept it to herself.

Cindy, who was not stupid, noted Jemma's silence and remarked with a disappointed sigh, 'Even if you had heard it, you wouldn't tell me, would you.' She halted at the door to her office. 'I wouldn't tell a soul, Jemma, honestly. I type your letters——'

Not all of them, Jemma thought. Some are so personal and private I type them myself. 'Now he's back,' she said, 'you'll probably hear soon enough.' She smiled. 'Thanks for telling me the man in question's come in from the cold. But I have to admit it's not my main aim in life to make his acquaintance.'

'You haven't *seen* him! When you have, you'll understand what I'm talking about.'

So the man called Arne Drummond had come back to the fold. It was true, Jemma reflected, that a story was circulating about him. He had been having a passionate affair with a woman called Johanna. The next thing the world apparently knew was that she had married Arne Drummond's rival in love, David Forrest.

Arne had abruptly left Prospect Industrial—although his return seemed to prove that his departure had been only temporary—and gone overseas.

Jemma stared through her window to the landscaped gardens which beautified the approach to the large modern building in which the company she worked for prospered and grew. It seemed that now Arne Drummond, having got the desertion of his ex-lover out of his system—if rumour had been right for once and he had quit the country for that purpose—had found himself ready to return and face the man who had married the woman he, Arne, had apparently loved.

Well, Jemma thought with a faint sigh, that was one problem that would not knock on her door, pleading to be solved. If he was indeed still suffering from a residue of despair, or even a badly battered psyche, Arne Drummond plainly was the type who could afford to attend the clinic of a top consultant psychiatrist.

A man with his considerable financial advantages, not to mention his elevated position in the business world, would hardly seek out the comforting shoulder of the company's counsellor, especially when that person was a young woman in her mid-twenties, seated at a desk in a small office tucked away in a corner of the entrance hall.

Jemma looked at her watch. In ten minutes' time, Tom from packaging would be coming to see her. Two minutes up to the staff eating-centre, four to drink some coffee, two down—and two to compose herself into the smiling, clear-thinking, infinitely understanding counsellor everyone expected her to be.

Calling to Cindy, she turned in the corridor to lock her door, wishing fleetingly that sometimes—just once would do—someone would enter her room with a happy smile and bring her some good news.

Starting her walk, she noticed absently that a man was striding towards her, executive case swinging. Automatically, her brain shifted into an analytical mode, and she classified the footsteps. They belonged to a man with no problems, who had charted his own course in life and who knew exactly where he was going—and why.

Eyes to the ground, she pressed on, conscious that the two minutes she had allocated for getting there were flying by.

'Is there something wrong?' A deep masculine voice brought her to a startled halt. The footsteps had ceased, their owner was addressing her.

She lifted her head and looked into eyes that were like the sea below a clear sky, blue and deep and fathomless. She went headlong into their depths, plunging, drowning, with as much chance of coming up for air as a diver floundering out of control.

Distractedly, her subconscious filled in the rest of his face. There was the strong nose, the broad forehead, the sweeping planes forming the cheeks; the stubborn chin, the sensitive fullness of the lips. Above all, there was the overpowering presence of the man.

Those lips were moving again. 'You look,' they were saying, 'as if you have the troubles of the entire population of the world on your shoulders.'

Jemma surfaced, gasping for air, control restored, her lifeline reconnected. Her face broke into a smile, lighting up her deeply brown eyes, uplifting her wide, warm mouth and parting her soft lips.

Shaking her head, her thick brown hair swinging, she answered, 'Not the entire population, only a very small section of it.' Glancing at her watch, she frowned. 'Oh, no. Three minutes left. I mustn't be late. Please excuse me.' Her feet raced each other to the stairs.

At the turn, she glanced back. The man was walking away as if he had only just resumed his journey. Oh, yes, he knew where he was going. And, by the proud angle of his head, Jemma judged that he would surely go there, wherever that was, alone.

Tom was not waiting when she returned. Going into Cindy's office, Jemma commented, 'Tall, broad and handsome?' Already, Cindy was nodding. 'With the most incredible blue eyes you could hope to see in a man?'

'Yes, yes. You've seen him? Isn't he fantastic? And guess what, he's still unattached. Can you believe that?'

Jemma laughed, believing it easily. What woman could keep up with that resolute stride? 'That won't last,' she answered. 'Some female will make a grab.' She sighed exaggeratedly. 'And will she get herself a dream man!' Her heart dipped unaccountably. 'I can imagine his requirements. A slinky, green-eyed blonde, gift-wrapped in twenty-two-carat gold and a beautiful body that never says "no".'

Cindy's laughter filled the room. 'Anyone would think you knew everything there was to know about love and sex. But *I* know,' she glanced at Jemma's ringless hands, 'that you know less about men than I do.' She waved her engagement ring and picked up a picture from her desk of a smiling young man, hugging it to her chest.

'Is that so?' Jemma smiled, letting her secretary think what she liked about her boss's private life.

Her long-standing boyfriend, Richard, had drifted into the background of her life now. His touch and his kisses had left her wanting more than he seemed able to give. Realising this, she had told him, 'It isn't working, Richard, is it? I like you a lot as a friend, but—well, we're just not right for each other, are we?'

Richard had been angry at first, refusing to accept her decision. When he had calmed down, he had declared, 'I want us to meet again some time, talk it over, see how you feel then.' But she was sure Richard had, deep down, accepted that, for a long time, their relationship had really had nowhere to go.

'My job has taught me a few things, Cindy woman-of-the-world Milton,' she returned, smiling.

'The sad things, Jemma, not the happy things.'

Cindy's perceptive remark made Jemma pause in the doorway. 'If everyone were happy, they wouldn't need me, would they?'

Jemma reached her desk as someone tapped on her door. 'Come in, Tom,' she called and pulled a folder towards her.

The following evening, Jemma sat at a table in the staff eating-centre, a cup of coffee in front of her. She had been working late and felt the need of a break before leaving for home. She took a mouthful and the coffee tasted hot and pleasant to her palate. Her thoughts drifted with the curling steam.

'You smile a lot,' a young woman in her office had said that evening. 'You make us feel better.' The girl, whose name was Pam, had dried her tears and stared at Jemma, at her dark brown hair, her oval-shaped face and warm, brown eyes. 'You give us all hope, Miss Hale. That's why we like talking to you. You never let us down.'

Jemma had shaken her head, too moved to speak.

Her own mother had once said, 'There's a sweet softness about you, dear, I don't think you realise. It's in your face, you know. A welcome look that says...' Her mother had shaken her head, at a loss for words. 'I think——' she had remarked, 'I think if I were in any kind of trouble, I wouldn't hesitate to come to you.'

'Why, Mum,' Jemma's eyes had grown moist, 'that's a beautiful compliment for a mother to pay her daughter. But then,' she had added, 'you might—just—be a little prejudiced?' Her mother had laughed and denied it.

If she took her work seriously—and she did—well, it was other people's lives she was dealing with. Didn't they deserve every bit of help, and as much of her time as she could give?

Now, she propped her head on her hand, hearing the voices around her, aware of the increase in numbers. Men, freed from the constraints of a board meeting, laughed and joked, filling trays with surprisingly good-quality food. Prospect Industrial was a successful international company. They could afford the best for their staff.

Jemma pushed back her chair and picked up her bag. Her car was at the garage being repaired and she would have to get a bus home.

'So, the White Rabbit is off again in her race against time?'

The deep voice, whose tones and cadences had echoed in her mind since she had heard them the day before, made her jerk up her head. He must have been at the meeting. What troubled her at that particular moment was the way his unexpected appearance was provoking such a whirlpool of feeling inside her. If, she told herself, she didn't pour the oil of reason on to it without delay, it would spell deep trouble for her well-being and peace of mind into the foreseeable future.

'W-White Rabbit?' was all she could think of saying until her composure returned to normal.

The blue eyes smiled, the laughter lines crinkling. 'You plunged me straight into the pages of *Alice in Wonderland* yesterday morning—looking at your watch and saying, "Oh no, three minutes left. I mustn't be late!"'

Jemma laughed, her heart racing this time instead of her feet. Which was infinitely to be preferred, since last time her hurrying feet had taken her away from him.

There was a pause, nervousness tensing her body, the sheer pleasure of seeing him again petrifying her thinking-processes.

'You've——' she moistened her lips, 'you've been at the meeting?'

It was an offering, at least, something to break the strange intensity which stretched between them.

'I chaired it. What about you?' His eyes were on her, assessing and searching.

It wasn't just their colour, nor the intelligence they held. There was something deep within them that saw— saw what? she wondered, half hypnotised, bewildered. What was it about the man that made her feel this way, almost as though a part of her had been missing all her life? And now it was here and waiting to be grafted on, and she knew that if this was denied her, she would never feel complete again.

'I've been working late.'

He frowned. 'Couldn't it have waited?'

'Sometimes, people are so worried, or unhappy, that their problems can't wait. This time it was a member of the domestic staff.'

He moved nearer to let someone pass. 'Were you able to help?'

'Only temporarily. She needs accommodation, some-where she can call home.'

He looked into her face again. 'I'd like to buy you a drink, Miss Hale. Not here. Somewhere more relaxing. I think we both deserve it. Will you come?'

'There's really no need——'

'I've been meaning to contact you, anyway. For——' his eyes swooped over her '—one reason or another. This way,' he invited, indicating the door.

'I mean it, Mr Drummond, there's no need for you to leave your colleagues.'

He smiled down at her. 'This time when the White Rabbit goes on her way, I want to go with her.'

In his car, she closed her eyes, leaning back on the plush upholstery, inhaling the leather smell and wondering how it was that she came to be in Arne Drummond's car, driving somewhere for a drink.

His shoulder was next to hers, filling the well cut jacket. His legs were extended, braking and manipulating the thrust of the engine. His thighs were full and taut with male strength and Jemma had to avert her eyes to neutralise the disturbing sensations the sight and proximity of his body aroused in her.

'How did you know my name?' Jemma ventured, her eyes appreciating the golden light of the sun as it made its way down the sky.

A lift of the broad shoulders told her how easy it had been to discover it. 'I made enquiries. You gave me clues. About the world's troubles, or some of them.'

Jemma smiled and caught the fleeting brightness in his eyes. There was a world in them, but not a troubled one, offering instead a tantalising vision of a very special heaven way outside her reach.

The bewildered feeling returned. What was she doing here, she wondered again, seated beside this unknown man, driving at speed to a destination which he knew— there was no doubt about that—but of which she was ignorant?

The car swung left on to a gravelled parking-area, crunching to a stop. Arne pushed out of the driving-seat and came round to her, opening her door. She straightened her skirt, looking round, unwilling to meet those eyes.

'This way, Miss Hale.' He ducked at the entrance to avoid the low beam, standing back as Jemma entered. At the bar, he stood beside her, his broad back pushing at the jacket of his grey business suit, around which still hung the ambience of the board room.

He turned to rest an elbow on the counter top, his white shirt twisting slightly to accommodate the expanse of his chest. Beneath it, Jemma's eyes picked up the shading in of dark hair, this glimpse into his purely private world raising her pulse-rate unbearably.

'What's your choice, Jemma?'

Her heart cartwheeled at the sound of her first name on his lips. Waiting for their order, Jemma stared through the windows, knowing his eyes were on her. What was it about her that attracted them so often? What was this thing between them they seemed to be in the middle of before it had even begun?

'We'll go outside,' he said, indicating the rear door. 'Shall we?' The question had been asked merely out of politeness.

She did not resent the fact that this man knew his own mind. It had already become obvious to her that he knew just where he was going in life. To her bewilderment, all she wanted in the whole world at that moment was to follow wherever he led.

The chair scraped on the paving stones, the table rang metallically as their glasses came to rest, the whiteness of the exterior furniture standing out with almost blinding clarity in that fading, gilded light.

Arne removed his jacket, draping it across the back of his chair. He sat, hand wrapped around his glass, his movements fluid as he took a drink, put it down, watching Jemma taste hers and move her tongue over her lips to savour the aftertaste.

A few feet away, the river flowed by. Mallards, the young ones trailing, made for the shelter of their nests. A pair of swans swam tranquilly near the further bank.

Trees rustled and whispered, and the lights strung high along the patio edge dropped their multi-coloured reflections to float on the water's surface, doubling the magic they gave to the scene.

From the inn, music came melodiously, romantic and sweet. The flowers gave out a release of perfume, drenching the air before closing up for the night. All Jemma's senses were drowned in sensation, heightened most of all by the nearness of the man who had brought her there.

If I didn't think I'd gone completely crazy, she thought, closing her eyes, I'd say that I'd fallen for him, tumbled hopelessly and totally in love.

'"Sweet Thames run softly,"' Arne quoted, leaning back, one shirtsleeved arm hanging loosely, watching her over the rim of his glass. 'Sweet Jemma smile at me.' His voice had lowered, his eyes had picked up the colour mix of the lights, and Jemma stared into them, fascinated.

'I don't understand,' she whispered.

His hand came out, covering hers. 'Tell me what you don't understand.' His eyes gleamed, their piercing blue running like a painter's well-used palette into the lights' rainbow of colours. 'Tell me your problems, Jemma. Unburden yourself to me. Learn by experience what your clients feel when they tell you about their unhappy lives and ask you to fit the pieces into a whole again.'

Bemused by his question, by everything about him, she answered, 'I don't have any problems.' But it wasn't true, was it, she asked herself, not any more. Until yesterday morning, her life had been like a long, straight road stretching into the far distance.

Overnight, mountains had been thrown up as if volcanic activity had hit her private plateau. Her road was not straight any longer, there were impossible gradients ahead for her to cope with, summits to reach and conquer before her way forward could become clear again.

And this man had been the cause, he was the volcano that had erupted into her life's calmness, and the burning lava of his eyes was rushing down towards her, threatening to swallow her whole.

He must have picked up her baffled state of mind. Leaning forward, arms folded on the table, he said softly, 'All I wanted to do in bringing you here was to take away the worry from your eyes.'

She found herself leaning towards him. 'Why should you be so concerned about me? I'm not your responsibility, am I? We move on different levels, both in life and in our work.'

A group emerged in single file from the rear door of the inn, laughing and talking, pushing at chairs until they reached a table across the patio. All the while, Arne had held Jemma's eyes, his fine mouth drawn into a taut smile.

He scraped back his chair. 'Come, Jemma.' Taking her hand, he led her to the patio's edge where it dropped away to the river.

Drawing her to his side, he eased her head sideways so that it rested on his shoulder. 'Let me confide in you, Jemma. You see,' he said huskily, 'I have a problem. I've fallen impossibly in love with a beautiful, compassionate woman, and I don't know if she feels the same. What would you do, Jemma, in my position?'

CHAPTER TWO

'ARNE? Darling?' The husky, feminine voice called from a few feet away. It held the faintest touch of uncertainty, a hint of hurt feminine pride.

Slowly, Arne turned, but his arm stayed around Jemma. A woman was standing by his chair, her palm stroking across the shoulders of his jacket, her hip pressed suggestively against the sleeve. Her dress was draped in folds around her, caught up in provocative places, revealing enticing expanses of her pale skin, the neckline plunging low.

Jemma had seen her in passing at the firm's offices, moving gracefully along the corridors, which was how she knew her name and her status. Dave Forrest, her husband, appeared to be missing from the crowd with whom she had come.

Arne nodded, unsmiling. 'Johanna.'

The woman's overbright eyes, shifting from him, burned Jemma up like the sun withering a leaf prematurely to autumnal brittleness. She moved slowly towards them, her body swaying, eyeing Jemma as if she would like to complete the process of destruction and crunch her underfoot.

'You've found yourself a new woman, darling,' Johanna Forrest remarked, her voice silky now. 'It didn't take you long after your return, did it?' Her head thrown back, she threw the full brilliance of her green eyes at his face.

Her artificially fair hair was piled high, her features enhanced to perfection by skilful make-up. Diamonds sparkled at her throat and ears, her left hand weighted with rings as it stroked its way down Arne's arm. The caressing movement his jacket had received began again, this time on the flesh-and-blood man.

Jemma, sick at heart, jerked away from the hand that was now gripping her shoulder. Was Johanna's touch affecting him so much he had to grit his teeth to withstand her enticement?

'I'll find my own way home, Mr Drummond,' Jemma said, forcing a smile. 'Please don't worry about me——'

'Jemma.' He caught at her arm but she slipped from his grasp, her smile vanishing.

Johanna watched the disagreement in fascination. 'She's saying "no", Arne?' the woman commented with mock disbelief. 'My God, darling, you must be slipping.'

'Jemma!' The lash of his anger reached across the patio. She had almost made it to the door. He was beside her now, swinging her to face him.

'Yes?' she responded, hearing the waver in her own voice.

'For God's sake.' He released her, looked round for his jacket and said, 'Wait there, please.'

Spoken in such a tone, it was impossible for an employee of Prospect Industrial to disobey the directive. Jemma watched as he jerked the iron seats out of his path and thrust into his jacket, making his way back to her.

From the centre of her group of friends, Johanna Forrest watched, lips pouting, her expression that of a woman scorned. Whatever she had done to Arne

Drummond in the past, Jemma concluded, she must have hurt him badly.

He sat in the driver's seat, knuckles white on the steering-wheel, cheek muscles working. 'Forgive me,' he said at last, 'for transferring my anger on to you.' He turned his head and in the light from the sunset's brightness, he said grimly, 'I should like you to forget that incident. Wipe it from your mind.'

Jemma affected a shrug. 'What happened was no concern of mine, Mr Drummond. You brought me out for a drink because you thought I could do with one——'

'The name's Arne.'

'Don't let your friend's unpleasant comments get to you, Mr Drummond,' she went on as if he had not spoken, 'I quite understand.'

'You do not understand!' His anger was all for her now. 'And I said, call me Arne.'

It took Jemma some time to answer. 'I can't,' she said at last. 'And what's more, I can't see any possible reason why I should. After this evening, we won't be meeting again except on a purely business basis.'

'We won't?' he queried distantly. 'That may be your considered, text-book view of our acquaintance. It isn't necessarily mine.'

It was the underlying sharpness in his tone that silenced Jemma, even though her heart went into a spin at the prospect of getting to know this enigmatic man better.

For a few moments, he stared through the windscreen. Fresh cars arrived, others drove away. Then, as if a decision had been made, he fired the engine and turned the car on to the road.

They were some distance into their journey before he broke the silence, his eyes on the traffic variations ahead. 'Will you direct me to where you live?'

It was a modern apartment block and he drove into the forecourt. 'Which flat is yours?' he asked, scanning the rows of windows.

'Third floor. Flat five.' He nodded, and Jemma, getting out, was startled when Arne prepared to follow her. At once, her innate politeness came into play, prompting her to say, 'Please come in.'

It needed little more than a cursory glance around her home, Jemma perceived, to enable Arne Drummond to shade in the gaps in his knowledge of her. Removing her jacket, she turned to him, a smile in place.

Their eyes held, his steady and penetrating, hers uncertain, unsure. In comparison with the overwhelming presence of this man, her ex-boyfriend Richard, pleasant and self-effacing, had faded into the wallpaper. Arne Drummond, shoulders broad, manner easy, hands pushed into the trouser pockets of his dark business suit, filled the room to its shaded corners. Her heartbeats tripped as his smile grew warmer, his eyes holding a mysterious message.

'It fits,' he commented with a smile, 'all this. Matter-of-fact, yet welcoming. Furnished practically, yet giving out a subtle warmth that says, sit down and take life as it comes. It blends perfectly with its owner's personality—well balanced, unassuming and unconsciously inviting. Is it yours or do you rent?'

'I own it, with my parents' help. Er——' She moistened her lips. This man, she discovered, had the effect of knocking logical reasoning out of her head. 'Coffee?' she asked. He smiled, plainly detecting her underlying nervousness.

'Why not?'

Following her to the minuscule kitchen, he leaned sideways, hands in pockets, against the archway that separated it from the living-area. He watched her, making her feel uncomfortable. She wished fervently that he would speak. I'm usually the one, she thought agitatedly, who does the observing, watching others movements, 'reading' them, making personality judgements.

'That member of staff you were interviewing this evening,' he remarked at last. 'She needs accommodation, you said?'

Jemma nodded, eyes hopeful. His glance met hers and no matter how hard she tried, she could not halt the swift rise of adrenalin it caused within her.

He took the tray, lowering it to a table. Occupying a chair, he leaned back, legs outstretched, eyes lazy as he watched her seat herself on the two-seater sofa opposite him. She wished he would end his observation of her. A dream picture floated across her inner vision, of this man in weekend clothes, totally at ease, belonging... For heaven's sake, she reproached herself severely, keep a rein on your fantasies, your ridiculous dreams!

'I know a place with a room vacant,' he said at last, taking a mouthful of coffee, his white teeth crunching the biscuit Jemma had offered. 'It belongs to my brother and his wife. They're abroad for a year or two and they've rented it out as a shared house. The tenants are mainly students. One's just quit.'

'It sounds perfect,' Jemma exclaimed. 'You're sure it hasn't been re-let?'

'Quite sure. I could give you the address of the agents in charge of the place in my brother's absence.'

'The rent—is that reasonable?' Arne nodded again. 'It sounds too good to be true.'

Unexpectedly, he rose, abandoning his cup, filling the space beside her, his wide, essentially male thighs touching hers. Taking her chin, he turned her face to catch the light from the table lamp which he had switched on in passing. 'Are those eyes less troubled now? Is Miss Hale smiling again?'

Jemma did smile, she couldn't help herself. 'I'm not sure,' she remarked, his proximity making all her senses work flat out, and her pulses leap like spring lambs for good measure, 'why you're acting the Good Samaritan and Father Christmas rolled into one.'

He smiled, saying nothing, yet all the while his eyes made a passionate speech.

'But I do appreciate it.' He continued to read her face, as closely as if he were committing it to memory. She was disconcerted, liking the touch of his fingers on her skin too much for her own good, and part of her wished he would go, the other part longing for him to stay.

'And,' she cleared her throat, feeling her colour mount, 'I've enjoyed the break this evening. Very much.' More than you'll ever know, she thought.

'She's showing me the door,' he commented without moving. 'Verbally, of course.' His smile came and went. 'We must do it again some time. Get together, I mean.' His attention was on her lips now, his hands cupping her face. 'You agree?'

Jemma, her breath strangely shallow, could only nod. Slowly, magically, his lips lowered to hers, lightly touching, lifting and touching again, then harder, parting them, as if he found the taste of them immensely to his liking.

'I didn't,' she found herself saying breathlessly, 'say "yes" to that.'

He released her, rising. 'Ah, but you did,' he answered enigmatically, 'in more ways than one. I repeat,' he added, gaze flicking over her, 'we must do it again some time. Agreed?'

'Agreed,' she answered lightly, matching her tone to his.

Next morning, he was there in the doorway, even before Cindy had put in an appearance.

Jemma stared at him, wondering for a ridiculous moment whether he was real. He had, after all, been with her all night in her dreams. 'Hi,' she offered, heart hammering. 'Can I help you?'

He came fully in, eyes mocking. 'I want to talk to Jemma, the woman, not Miss Hart, professional counsellor.' So he hadn't brought his 'problem' to her. Which was a relief, she thought, relaxing as much as her pounding heart would allow.

Smiling at his comment, she half swung in her chair, easing back her jacket as if it were a low-cut evening gown and crossing her legs encased in dark stockings, which his gaze immediately dived to. 'That better?'

'Provocative, too.' His eyes lifted, full of masculine appreciation, to the thrust of her breasts straining against the satin sheen of her blouse. Colouring, she returned to normal. 'Well, well,' he drawled. 'So there's another side to Miss Hale which shows she's human, after all. Not to say,' his gaze raked her again, 'warm and womanly. And sensual.'

Jemma cleared her throat, hearing Cindy's voice in the corridor. 'Did you want——?'

Hands flat on the desk, he leaned forward, an action which brought his face disconcertingly near. 'Are you free this evening?'

Jemma's heart jumped madly. He was asking her to meet him socially again, and so soon?

'I want to talk to you.'

About that 'problem' of his, she wondered?

'Also, I didn't give you the address of my brother's house agents. Mainly because I thought I ought to show you the place. You should inspect it, shouldn't you, before recommending it?'

'Strictly, yes.'

'So you're free?'

'Well, I should do some paperwork,' she began, 'but——'

'Ah, I was waiting for that "but". Seven o'clock? I'll pick you up.' He was gone, just like a dream cut off by the alarm clock.

It would be a mixture of business and—work, not pleasure, surely, Jemma pondered, wondering what to wear. He had told her that he wanted to talk to her, hadn't he? 'Let me confide in you,' he had said as they had stood by the river last night, then Johanna had appeared and the subject had obviously gone right out of his thoughts.

When he stood in the tiny entrance lobby to her apartment, his admiring eyes told her that she had chosen the right clothes to wear. So he liked the peach-coloured dress with its low-buttoning front and small turnover collar, its short sleeves that revealed the smooth skin of her arms, her white earrings and heavy white beads to match.

Scanning his face, uncaring whether or not her excitement at seeing him again was showing, she commented impishly, 'This is Jemma Hale, the woman. Or have you come to see Miss Hale, the——?'

A light flared in his eyes and he wrapped his arms around her, hugging her tight against him and giving her a kiss that left her breathless. 'That, Jemma Hale, *all woman*,' he clipped, 'is what you get for cheeking the boss.'

'Just joking,' she answered, unsure now.

'I know.' His eyes caressed her features, while his hand stroked back her hair. 'You should do it more often. It gets a man——'

'Going?' she interposed with an impudent grin.

His eyes narrowed. 'We know all about the male of the species, do we, Miss *counsellor* Hale?' Then he gathered her to him again and this time his hands moved down her back, to her hips and sliding up her arms to rest fleetingly on her breasts.

This man, she thought, oh, this man, he's all I'd ever want . . .

'I've fallen in love,' he had told her last night. Stiffening at the memory, she made to draw away and he let her go, his expression unreadable. If she had disappointed him she was sorry, but she refused to be any woman's stand-in. *Impossibly* in love, he had said, hadn't he? Which to her trained mind meant a problem crying out to be solved.

'Is it far?' she asked, making an effort to lift herself above the situation and regain her professional detachment. With this man, it seemed to be her only defence.

'To the house? About ten minutes by car.' He sounded a little offhand. Was he annoyed with her for withdrawing, both from his arms and from the distinctly dangerous warmth which his kisses had begun to generate?

It was a spacious residence he showed her, solidly and generously built, and well furnished, too.

'It's just great,' she commented, back in the car. 'I wish all the owners of places recommended to me had standards as high as your brother's!'

'Good,' he said. 'Glad to be of help.' At some traffic lights, he produced a card. 'The house agent's name and number.'

'I don't know how to thank you,' she remarked, taking the card and glancing at him.

'You don't?' he asked drily, meeting her eyes for an electrifying second. Her skin prickled at the meaning in them. The thought of lying in this man's arms left her mentally gasping and rent with longing. This feeling, of physically as well as mentally needing to be close to a man, was something she had never experienced before, and it bewildered her, being almost beyond her control.

In the parking area behind the block of flats, someone wound down the window of a nearby car as Arne drew to a stop.

'Eaten yet?' Arne asked, cutting the engine.

'No, but I've got food in the house. And some wine——'

'Are you intending to invite me to share this dissolute feast?'

'Well, I——'

'Jemma?' Knuckles tapped on the window. Shaken by Richard's sudden appearance, Jemma made to scramble out.

Arne asked distantly, 'A client of yours?'

'No, my boyfriend.' She realised her mistake. 'I mean my——'

'Pardon me,' he said icily, 'for intruding on a purely private occasion. You should have told me you were not free this evening, after all. Or were you intending to play us off against each other? I'm sorry to spoil the fun you were no doubt anticipating,' he added grimly, reaching for the ignition switch, 'but——'

He was dismissing her, all boss and businessman.

'You've got it wrong,' she exclaimed, striving to correct her mistake and put things right between them. 'I meant to say he's my *ex*-boyfriend.'

He ignored her statement. 'I'm happy to have been of some assistance in your job.' He was Prospect's top man without doubt now, and as unreachable as a distant star. Light-years away...

Icicles dripped down Jemma's spine. 'Thank you for your help,' she said, making an effort to match his coolness with hers. But he had relegated her in a few seconds to mere employee, and her attempt to equal his dismissive tone was a dismal failure. Since he was making it unmistakably clear that he no longer wanted her company, she had no choice but to get out.

Facing Richard on the forecourt, she asked in a tight voice, 'Did you want me for something?'

'It's two months,' he said. 'We agreed to meet again to see if we could patch things up. And I've brought your key back, but I'll keep it if you think we——'

'Oh, but——' Jemma broke in, swinging round when Arne's engine roared to life. Seconds later, he had gone.

Jemma had not seen Arne for more than ten days. It seemed like half a lifetime. She had spent her working hours watching for him along every corridor, round every corner.

At home, she had listened for the ring of the telephone, quite pointlessly, she knew, but hoping all the same that he might just have thought sufficiently well of her to have looked up her number and called her.

Then she had reminded herself that someone else had, on his own confession, captured his heart; that although he might legally be free, emotionally he was tied. Maybe he hadn't, after all, managed to exorcise Johanna Forrest from his feelings?

'A problem', he had called the woman he had fallen for so hopelessly. She was beautiful, he had said. All of which could be applied to his ex-fiancée. 'Impossible' was how he had described his love—wasn't she married now to someone else? And beautiful Johanna certainly was. But he had used another word—'compassionate'. That didn't fit, Jemma accepted—unless, from his intimate experience of her in the past, he knew differently.

One day, on leaving the eating-centre after lunching there, Jemma collided with a man coming through the doorway. As she extricated herself, her flushed face stared up unbelievingly into Arne's expressionless face. She apologised profusely, but he merely nodded as if she were a passing acquaintance.

Although she had continually been looking out for him, his sudden appearance, plus the fleeting contact with his hard, lean frame, shook her entire nervous system. The coldness in his gaze made her shiver.

He stood back politely to let her pass, but she found herself trapped by his eyes, searching them for the magic they had held for her before. The magic was still there and they were still intensely blue, but it was the colour of clashing steel.

'Pam,' her lips were moving against her wishes and she found herself addressing him, 'the homeless girl you helped——'

He looked steadily at her, no movement in his face.

'Miss Hale,' someone passing interrupted, apologising, 'will you see me today? I need help with——'

'Yes, yes, four-thirty this afternoon?' Jemma spoke hastily, afraid that Arne would go on his way.

'Well,' she turned back to him quickly, 'she—Pam—you remember now?' Her eyes pleaded with him to give some sign of recollection. 'She's very happy in your brother's house. It's like a palace to her, she said. It's warm and weatherproof and wonderful, she told me.' She searched his eyes for reaction. 'She'd been sleeping rough, you see. She wasn't welcome at home any more...'

At last he responded—with a nod.

'I had to tell you, Mr Drummond, to thank you again. You were so good about it...' Her voice tailed off.

'Jemma,' Cindy called in a stage whisper, 'just slipping out to do some shopping. Won't be long.'

By the time Jemma had acknowledged her secretary's remark, Arne had gone.

Jemma was at her desk staring unseeingly at a pile of letters when Cindy returned. She did not burst in as she usually did, filling the place with her exuberance. Instead, she stood in the doorway staring.

She was so quiet, Jemma looked up. 'Anything wrong, Cindy?'

'If I hadn't seen it with my own eyes,' Cindy said slowly, 'I wouldn't have believed it.'

Jemma's heart began to thud. 'Believed what?'

'The way you were looking at him. As if you——' She shook her head as though it would have been too stupid to give voice to the words.

Jemma did not ask who her secretary was talking about. That would have been too ingenuous. Instead, she picked up a bulldog clip and pressed it open and shut, watching its jaws widen and snap. Was I that transparent, she wondered with dismay. If Cindy could see it, who else did?

'Are you, Jemma?' Cindy sounded both incredulous and concerned.

Jemma hunched a shoulder. 'What if I am? It'll pass.'

The telephone rang and Cindy dived to answer it, handing it to Jemma. When the call was finished, Cindy drifted back. 'How, Jemma—I mean there's more to it, isn't there, than just worshipping from afar? I could almost hear the air sizzling between you.'

'You could?' Jemma looked at her with hope. Then she shook her head. 'It's one-sided. He took me for a drink one evening after work. I looked tired, he said, needed a break.' Her smile was faint. 'He also helped me with an accommodation problem. He was just being the considerate employer.'

'He was?' Cindy's frown was unbelieving as she made for her office.

Saturdays Jemma usually spent doing domestic jobs. It was midday and, taking a rest, she half reclined on the sofa, easing off one sandal, then the other. There was dust on her cotton slacks and her patterned T-shirt had faded with constant washings.

Running her fingers through the untidy mop her hair had become, she wondered what people would say if they saw the poised and reliable Miss Hale they habitually confided in so dishevelled.

When the entryphone sounded, she jumped, not expecting a caller. Lifting the phone, she asked, 'Who—who's that?'

'Arne Drummond,' came the curt reply. 'Will you let me in?'

It was a command she could not disobey, coming from one of the top men at Prospect Industrial. This, she informed herself firmly, was certainly not the man who had held her in his arms and kissed her, so she must treat him as he obviously wanted to be treated—as employee to employer. With shaking hands she released the door catch. Moments later, he stepped in and her heart rebelled at the restraint she had placed on it and bounded at the sight of him.

Beneath his jacket, the dark jersey-knit shirt closed around his upper body, revealing its surface hardness. His belted fawn trousers were just as well fitting, causing Jemma to shift her gaze with speed to his face, although the forceful good looks she found there caused her pulses to trip just as madly as the sight of the rest of him.

Inviting him into the living-area, she turned to face him. There was a tension in her limbs, a strange shyness cementing her thoughts. She could not even make herself slip into her smoothly professional role and extract some measure of poise from that.

Dressed as carelessly as she was—and with bare feet, too—she was in no position to draw herself up to her full height, which was not all that high, anyway, and square up to the man who had invaded her private territory. For this was a stranger who looked down at her, not the tender man who had wanted to make her smile, helping her to forget the problems her job presented her with.

All the time she was struggling with her feelings, he watched her. Curiously, it was as if he were a climber learning by heart an untried route to a mountain's summit.

'Would you——' her voice was hoarse, so she cleared it, 'would you like a drink, Mr Drummond?' Something inside her told her it would be a liberty to call *this* man by his first name. They were not, it seemed, on those terms any more.

He eyed a chair and, without asking, took it. Bemused, Jemma watched him.

'No drink, thanks,' he said.

She looked down at herself. 'If you'd told me you were coming, I'd have——'

'What's wrong with the clothes you're wearing?' He slid lower in the seat, his legs outstretched. As if he belonged, she thought bemusedly. Just as it had been in that daydream she had had the last time he was there . . .

'I've come to see the woman who lives here,' he commented lazily, his eyes running all over her, right down to her bare feet, *'the woman,'* he emphasised, 'not her twin self, the professional smiling machine.' He glanced around, expression cynical. 'Being the weekend, I did wonder if I'd be interrupting something.'

Out of all proportion this nettled her because of its barely disguised innuendo. She snapped, pulling on her sandals, 'I told you, I've broken with my boyfriend. The other evening he just brought my key back.'

'That wasn't what I heard him say. He seemed to be wanting to start again where you'd left off. Did he enjoy your cooking?' His mouth curved but his eyes stayed cold.

'I didn't invite him in. He went home. We decided against coming together again. The decision was mutual.'

He nodded, his smile this time holding the merest hint of warmth. 'What do I have to do to coax my hostess to sit down in her own home?'

She made for a chair but, still unable to settle, she plumped up a cushion and unnecessarily straightened a framed pencil sketch on the wall. Turning, she found him watching her. She rubbed her hands against each other, aware that every one of her actions was being noted by him, which only unnerved her all the more.

At last, she sat down, in the centre of the sofa. For days she had longed for a sight of him, for the sound of his voice. Now he was there, in her home, she found herself seeking desperately for a way of re-establishing contact—not physical, that was out of the question, she knew that now, but verbal would do very well. But it was as if they were complete strangers again, not even acquaintances, on different sides of a very high fence— boss and employee.

Well, that was what they were, wasn't it—strangers? They had had a drink together, then she had given him coffee. And he had solved a client's problem for her. How had she come to build so much on such trivial incidents? So what if he had kissed her—to this man what were a few kisses in passing?

Arne removed his eyes from her to consult his watch. 'Do you ever go to a pub for lunch?'

Jemma was stricken with embarrassment. 'I'm so sorry.' She got to her feet and glanced at her watch, too. 'Like me, I expect you haven't eaten yet. I——' The thought of entertaining Arne Drummond, high-powered executive, to lunch somewhat daunted her. But sitting there, eyebrow lifted, he looked a reasonable if sardonic example of a human being. 'Unless, of course, you'd rather go elsewhere?' Had she misunderstood him? Had the casual comment not included her, after all? 'On your own, of course. Then,' she invented hastily, to cover her gaffe, 'you could return here and see me about whatever you came to—er—see me about.'

She had made the statement into a question, but he did not supply the answer.

'Your suggestion suits me fine.' He continued to lounge back in the chair that was too small for him. 'A sandwich or two would suffice.' His normally slightly aloof features softened into a smile. 'I'll even offer to make them.'

'No need, Mr Drummond. I've got a couple of cheese and onion flans, plus salad, and—er—some raspberry mousse.'

'Home-made?'

'The mousse is freezer-made. Sorry. Next time——' She swallowed a gasp.

'Next time,' he cut in smoothly, 'I'll bring my own.'

Retreating to the kitchen, Jemma laughed, relieved that he had not taunted her for her second gaffe of the day. Of course there wouldn't be a 'next time'. She dived into the fridge. 'There's a stray can of beer at the back here,' she called from the cold interior. 'Would you like it?'

'Not at the moment, thanks.' She jumped at hearing his voice behind her. 'Later, perhaps.'

Withdrawing her head from the fridge, she twisted from her crouching position, noting that he had removed the casual jacket he had been wearing. 'Later?' She peered up his length to find him looking down at her, a curious smile playing about his lips.

'Yes, why not? Or have you got a date? A new boy-friend, perhaps?'

Rising and closing the fridge door, she shook her head, then pushed at her hair.

'Were you planning to do anything else?'

'Only to wash this.' He looked at her hair and she flushed at his narrow-eyed expression.

Mesmerised, she watched his hand come out, felt it run through her hair and press back her head, saw his mouth approach, his face slant, felt his lips' pressure. Then it was gone.

It was vitally necessary, she told herself, to keep her head. This man was only human, business tycoon though he was. And there was Johanna. And that other woman he had told her about.

She, Jemma Hale, was attractive to him—she supposed she was by the way he looked at her—only because she represented pastures new, and was therefore a challenge. She, who gave advice to others and expected them to listen to it, must listen to her own advice to herself. *Keep your head, keep your distance,* her wise self said. Feeling as I do about him, she answered, for heaven's sake, how am I expected to do that?

All the while she had been thinking, his eyes had never left her. They ran over the lips he had just kissed as if he were recalling how they had felt against his.

'Cool but unresponsive,' he commented, eyeing her narrowly. 'Where's the warm and sexy woman I kissed a couple of weeks ago? Has she moved away from this address while I've been abroad on business?'

So that was where he had been, not just keeping away from her! Relief flooding her heart, she smiled, eyes lighting up.

'That's better, Miss Hale,' he commented satirically. 'I prefer the woman in you to the stiff and starchy counsellor.'

'I'll—I'll get the food,' she said, tearing her gaze from his.

They ate their meal at the gate-legged table Jemma had opened out to one side of the living-area. They talked of Arne's journey across the world in the year or so that he had been away.

'I went to Indonesia and Japan, Africa,' he told her, 'South America...many other places.'

'For the company?' Should she have asked? He did not seem to mind.

'For Prospect. Plus my own enlightenment.'

As she listened, Jemma wondered at the extraordinary set of circumstances in which she found herself— lunching, simply and unpretentiously, with a man who until the last ten days or so had been merely a name to her; yet who, when he had materialised, had come to fill most of her waking thoughts.

Later, Jemma curled herself into the small chair, while Arne lounged on the sofa, legs extended, arms uplifted, hands clasped behind his head. He seemed to be lost in thought. He did not seem to expect her to entertain him and Jemma was glad. She wondered bemusedly, yet again, how it was that he came to be there at all.

Her eyes, shielded by her lashes, rested secretly on him. Seeing the character in his facial structure, the resolution in his chin and the firm set of his mouth, her heart acted strangely. He had loosened his tie and his shirt sat tautly across his shoulders. The belt around his waist revealed no surplus flesh, his well-fitting trousers wrapping around his hips.

Jemma guessed that when a woman put her arms around him and looked to him for strength and security, she would find it there beyond doubt. Yet there was, she was certain—she had noticed the first time they had met—an element in his make-up which no woman would be able to capture: his inner self, his secret being, something that was elusive and entirely private, nurtured and cherished by the man himself.

I want to be the one to try, she discovered herself thinking, then curled her fingers into her palms at her headstrong thoughts, I want to creep behind the front he shows to the world...

He changed position, giving her a small shock, twisting his hips and crossing his legs. His hand came out towards her. Her fingers uncurled, her instincts ready to comply, to reach out, make contact, but reason acted as a brake. Her fingers clenched again.

She told herself that she should know what to do. How many times had she advised and guided, suggesting ways out of problematical situations?

'Will you tell me something?' she asked, staring at his hand. The upraised eyebrows invited her to go ahead. 'Will you tell me why you've called on me today?'

He got to his feet, straightening the intimidating length of him, his long legs taking him towards her. He came to a stop, hands in pockets, looking down at her.

'Two reasons. Yesterday at work I met a woman in a doorway. She was leaving, I was arriving for a meal. We hadn't met for a couple of weeks. It was an empty two weeks for me. How had it been for her? I looked into her eyes and she told me.'

'No, I didn't!' Then she blushed, having assumed that she was the woman he was talking about.

'She told me something—I didn't really take it in.' His mouth was smiling, his eyes were the old piercing, hypnotic blue. 'All I saw was the longing in her eyes, the unhappiness behind them—and the hope behind that.'

'If I hadn't seen it with my own eyes,' Cindy had said, 'I wouldn't have believed the way you were looking at him. As if you...'

Jemma looked away, curling her toes. 'I'm sorry,' she said flatly, 'if I embarrassed you. Call it pressure of the job, a—a wish to thank you for your help. You——' she swallowed, 'you shouldn't have bothered to come here just because I—because I overdid my expression of gratitude.'

He knew she was lying, of course. He crouched down to match her eye level and took hold of her shoulders, massaging them with his thumbs.

'Look at me, Jemma.' He stared deeply into her eyes, searching, questioning. Then he hauled her up by the armpits so that she was forced to uncurl her legs and stand in front of him.

A moment later she was deep in his embrace, his mouth following the example of his eyes, penetrating the barrier of her lips and exploring her mouth's inner sweetness.

Lifting his head, he said softly, 'There was another reason why I came, Jemma. I had to talk to you.'

Her heart, having soared, dived to rock bottom. He wanted to consult her in a professional capacity. She withdrew from his arms and he let her go. 'There was no need to have done—what you've just done.' He waited for her to go on. 'Kissed me. Just because I gave you a certain look, one you interpreted as an invitation, but which I wasn't even aware of giving.'

He closed the gap and turned her to face him, his liquid gaze sending electrified darts through her body. She lowered her lids so that he could not see his effect on her.

'If I kiss a woman,' he said, 'there's usually a good reason.'

Now her eyes grew stormy. 'Sexual attraction, or to put it more crudely, bodily lust.' Somehow she had to hurt him as he was hurting her. 'I may not possess your experience in worldly matters, I might even seem, on your scale of values, an innocent where man and woman relationships are concerned, but I'm not a fool, nor am I ignorant. If I did—look at you in a certain way, maybe it was because I——' it was a lie she was going to tell again '—because I was feeling frustrated.'

He turned away angrily, stared at the inexpensive carpet with which she had furnished the place, then turned back.

'Missing the boyfriend, you mean?' It came out bitterly, she had never heard him use such a tone. Well, she had set out to annoy him and she had succeeded.

He seemed to regain his emotional balance and turned back. Incredibly, he was smiling. 'So angry she is, and all because I kissed her.'

He was downgrading the act, relegating to a triviality the invasion of her senses, the arousal of her desires. Which could only mean that she was over-reacting, which was something she constantly warned her clients about. It was only a kiss, he was saying. What's that nowadays between a man and a woman? All along, she reproached herself, she had been reading too much into everything he had said and done.

Gathering her scattered wits—his kiss had knocked them sideways—she stood uncertainly, wondering when the interview session was going to start.

There was a movement and fingers lifted her chin. The renewed touch of him had her skin prickling. 'You're as vulnerable as the rest of them, aren't you,' he commented softly. 'You can play the worldly-wise, dispassionate adviser as much as you like, but deep down I doubt if you'll ever change from the soft-hearted, susceptible young woman you really are.'

She met his unfathomable look, wanting that fine mouth to play havoc with hers again. To disguise her longing, she answered with a touch of pique, 'You can read me as if my thoughts were printed on a page. Yet,' she searched his eyes and foundered at the barrier of their inscrutability, 'I can't even guess what is going on in your mind.'

'Don't even try, Jemma.' He released her, breaking contact, leaving her cold and lonely.

She challenged him, 'How do you expect me to give you advice, to help to solve your problems if you don't come clean with me?'

His eyes narrowed, the slits that were left compressing their brilliance so that Jemma felt almost blinded, as if she were looking at the sun. 'Come clean with you?'

She was shaken by his steely tone. 'I meant it in general terms.' She looked at him askance. 'What's wrong? Do you have something to hide?'

For a moment he looked as if he wanted to hit out. She was used to such a reaction from people who consulted her when, in her questioning, she deliberately touched on a vulnerable spot to force them to be honest with her.

He recovered and smiled. 'Yes, I have something to hide. I shall tell my counsellor in my own good time.' He contemplated her pale cheeks and tightly pursed mouth. 'You've gone all professional on me.'

She did not answer, merely continuing to stare into his eyes, bracing herself against the pull of their enticing depths.

'When your clients come to see you,' he went on, 'I'm told you're charm itself. So where's the smile that's my due as a seeker of your advice?'

How can I smile at him, she asked herself fretfully, when he's going to tell me he loves another woman— the snag being, of course, that she's already married, or engaged, or any of the other permutations I've heard so often? I wish this consultation were over and done with, then I could get on with living my life as it was before I met him.

'You can talk to me now,' she prompted, glancing at the clock on the mantelshelf. 'I was going to do some paperwork this afternoon, but——'

'If I take you to my home, will you stop acting so primly?'

Talk to him in the privacy of his residence, wherever that was, about another woman—why else would such a man need advice?—a woman who was worrying him so much he had chosen her, Jemma Hale, to advise him rather than consult an established expert?

'Your home?' she queried. 'But why?'

'I can see no reason why not.'

Trying to conceal the excitement the prospect of seeing him again so quickly had caused, she answered matter-of-factly, 'No reason at all. What time would be convenient for you?'

His lips tightened at her professional manner. Pulling on his jacket, he said, 'Six-thirty this evening? I'll call for you.'

She nodded, seeing him to the door. For a brief moment he turned to look at her. Then he left, and there was an emptiness about the place that Jemma had not noticed before. But, and she hugged the knowledge to herself, he had sought *her* advice, no one else's.

More important, in less than three hours' time she would be seeing him again.

CHAPTER THREE

HE arrived half an hour early. She had showered and was wearing a white bath-robe, having been unable to decide which outfit to wear. How should she regard it, she wondered—as a social occasion, or a purely business interview?

Neither description applied, she decided, since it was the weekend. All the same, the venue might be Arne Drummond's home, but his invitation had not implied that he would be 'entertaining' her, just asking her advice.

Holding her head in dismay, she heard him identify himself. Opening the door, she remonstrated, 'I didn't expect you yet.'

She looked up at him as he filled the small living-room and was flustered to find that he was looking her over, appreciation glinting at her curving shape. She shivered as though he were actually touching her.

'I didn't know what to wear,' she told him, chin lifted high, 'which is why I'm wearing this. Please don't interpret it again as an invitation.'

He laughed, and it was a warm and reassuring sound. 'There's no need to be on the defensive, Jemma, about your own beauty. Just looking at you fills me with an unqualified pleasure.'

She did not take the remark as meaning her personally. By 'you' she told herself he meant 'you as a woman' not 'you as Jemma Hale'.

'Thank you,' she replied, hoping that her no-nonsense tone would underline her declaration that the way she was dressed—or underdressed—was pure chance. 'That still doesn't help me decide what to wear.'

He smiled and came close, outlining her body's shape with his palms, leaving a tingling trail although he had not touched her. He glanced at the robe's overlapped front as if his immediate instinct was to unwrap it. Instead, his hands stilled and stiffened as if that were the only way he knew of preventing them from following their overpowering inclination.

'Go and dress. Wear whatever you like. There'll only be the two of us.'

Running upstairs, she pulled on her under-garments, telling herself her haste was purely for self-protective reasons. Her skin felt singed, as if he had really made love to her.

The dress she chose was an autumn print wrap-around, crossing flatteringly between her breasts and falling in gentle folds from the waist. It was dressy to a point, yet unfussy enough to take a heart-to-heart in its stride, were she to find herself having to don her professional manner and hand out reassurance and encouragement, rigidly hiding her own feelings in the matter.

A long silver chain bearing an attractive pendant emphasised the separation of her breasts, while silver earrings swung provocatively from her ears.

Combing her hair, she tamed its curling softness. There was so much colour in her cheeks that she tried to tone it down. Her excitement at his presence was showing, whether or not she wanted it to.

Stepping slowly down the stairs, she saw him looking up at her. 'Have I chosen right?'

'I preferred you as you were,' he answered with a glint, 'but if I say you look beautiful, will that do?'

She smiled. 'I expect you say that to all the women you invite to dine with you.'

'A different one each night,' he joked. 'They almost tread on each other's heels. Why else do you think I need to consult Prospect Industrial's counsellor?' His manner changed. 'Let's go, Jemma. Do you have a jacket?'

He helped her lift it round her, then whispered her name. Turning her head, she found her mouth captured by his and her whole body throbbed in response to the demand in his lips.

In his car, she was conscious of the etched line of his profile, the well defined nose, the firm set of his mouth.

Soon, they were caught up in the traffic passing through the city's streets, then Arne took the car at speed along a fast road, turning off to climb a winding hill to reach a quieter area, a fashionable and expensive suburb.

The approach was along a driveway bordered by shrubs and young trees. The residence itself—it would have been demeaning to call such a place a mere house— was probably some forty years old. Its size was not the only thing that made Jemma catch her breath. The grounds on each side appeared to broaden out to the size of a park.

At the top of a short flight of steps, there was a porti-coed porch around the front entrance, announcing to doubters, if by then there were any, that this was a place of quality they were being invited to enter.

The entrance hall struck an individual if faintly awe-inspiring note, with its black and white floor tiles, its wall paintings and, centrally placed, a totem pole, almost certainly acquired, Jemma concluded, on Arne's wanderings. Fixed to the walls were other curious objects, and Jemma found her breath sufficiently to ask, 'I suppose you collected these on your recent journey around the world.'

'Some. Most I've had for quite a while.' He smiled fleetingly. 'A hobby of mine. Do they make you want to run for cover?'

'Oh no.' Jemma answered as though she meant it. 'I find them fascinating.' She smiled up at him. 'Is the rest of your home like this?'

'I'm relieved you can still look on it as a home after the primitive welcome these things give you. Some people—I won't name them—look so scared I get the feeling they'd rather turn round and leave than take another step inside.'

She looked straight into his eyes, but her gaze ricocheted away from their brilliance. Otherwise she would have drowned in them again and at that moment—not to mention for the rest of the evening—she needed to stay in control of her emotions, not to flounder in his fathomless depths.

'It shows me,' she told him, eyes wandering everywhere, 'another side of you. I would never have guessed you were anything but a tough-skinned businessman, assessing everything from the point of view of profit and loss, except,' her bright eyes challenged him, 'that "loss" probably doesn't have a place in your vocabulary.'

'That's a slightly impudent view of me, Miss Hale.' The glint was there again, sparking off her mouth, her throat, her breasts.

'Is it?' She smiled up at him. 'It was intended as an observation, not an insult. Really, I don't know you at all.'

'Not at all,' he answered drily. He gestured to the objects decorating the hall. 'Since you've mentioned profit, would you regard these as collectors' items?'

'You mean do I think you bought them with an eye to their appreciation over the years? Oh, no.' Her answer was emphatic. 'You didn't buy them with your head. You bought them with your heart.'

There was a long silence. Jemma, feeling the sudden tension, studied the strange wood carvings and mystical objects on the walls.

'Thanks for that,' he said softly behind her.

'No trouble,' she answered with a quick catch in her throat, glancing at him over her shoulder. 'Instant psychological analysis is the story of my life.' Had she lightened the atmosphere? It seemed so, since he was smiling.

He led her from room to room. There were so many. Each one had its own individual style. Most had their floor-to-ceiling bookshelves stacked with volumes.

'Have you a favourite artist?' she asked, looking closely from one framed painting, one piece of sculpture to another. 'There seems to be a certain similarity of style running through them. Yet,' she moved into another room, one which Arne had referred to as his study, 'others are quite different in concept. How did you get all these pieces here?'

She picked up a small carving, but whether it was intended to represent the male or the female of the species she could not decide. It was, she concluded, an abstract piece out of the artist's imagination. He—or she—was either a near genius, or a mere beginner. She wished she was more knowledgeable about art in all its forms, as Arne seemed to be.

'I brought them back with me from my travels. I've made quite a number of forays into primitive societies. They do exist, even in these so-called enlightened times. I told you I'd travelled around. I've got a few more years to my credit than you have, Jemma. Eight more.'

'You're older than I am, yet you expect me to give *you* advice?'

'You think that because I've lived longer, I should know all the answers?'

'Quite a few that I don't.' They were back in the living-room, where provision for comfort prevailed over primitive culture. 'I've been trained in my subject,' Jemma added. 'I suppose that gives me some advantage over your experience of the world. But mine's mostly theory, whereas yours, compared with mine, is practice. At this stage in my career,' she frowned, 'I haven't decided which is the more useful.'

Arne motioned her to one of the two sofas which faced each other square to the fireplace. He said, opening a cabinet, 'A drink before our meal? I know your choice.'

As he carried her glass across the room, the poignant sounds of a classical guitar drifted from a stereo system.

'It's my kind of music too,' Jemma remarked appreciatively, then rested her head to let the flowing sounds course through her. She felt the sofa give under Arne's weight and his proximity heightened the colour of the liquid sounds coming from the guitarist's gifted fingers.

'Tell me about Jemma Hale.'

She looked at him quickly, hearing the warmth in his tone, seeing the even warmer gaze stroking upwards from the neckline of her dress. Through the dreamlike haze which the music had created in her mind she tried to focus on his question.

He must have seen her confusion and helped her. 'For instance, how far did you progress education-wise?'

She wrinkled her nose. 'I don't like talking about myself.'

'You prefer listening to other people pouring out their troubles?'

She nodded. 'Well, my parents did their best to get me to go to university. I was worried about money, you see. In the end, I agreed to go. Now, I'm glad. I took a degree in social sciences, then spent a year as a social worker.'

'Did your university background prepare you for the shock of meeting the real thing during that year?'

'No way. What I saw in those twelve months shook me to the core.' She sighed. 'I still can't get adjusted to the way so many people mismanage their lives.'

'But you, Jemma Hale, have arranged your life to perfection?'

'I suppose you could say that.' She did not look at him.

He got to his feet, but stood close, looking down at her. 'You've got your future planned to the last detail? Career-girl all through. Men may come and go in your life, but marriage is on the banned list? Sex without the love that gives the act of love a meaning?' There was an abrasiveness in his voice that took her by surprise.

'I——' Her eyes lifted to his. 'Some time ago I made a decision about the direction I wanted my life to take. I haven't altered my mind about that...' The resolve that should have been behind the words was missing.

She had been quite certain—before she had met him. But the comfortable plateau that had been her life was unrecognisable now he had erupted on to the scene. It was a wilderness by comparison and she was lost in it, the straight path of career and job that had stretched ahead of her obliterated by the after-shocks of his appearance in her life.

She found herself staring into his eyes and she was drowning again, being drawn down and down. She was out of her depth and struggling for air.

He was pulling her into his arms, roping her to him. His mouth took control and he was tasting the essence of her, swallowing her moistness. Momentarily she managed to free her mouth, gasping at his action, but before her gasp was over, it had been drawn back into his consuming kiss. When he finally lifted his head, she was throbbing, every muscle and nerve inside her reaching out to him.

'Jemma, Jemma,' he said against her hair, 'do you know what you do to a man?'

She whispered, forehead against the smooth fabric of his shirt, 'Maybe I do, maybe I don't. You can tell me if you like.'

The laugh he gave rumbled under his ribs. 'In what capacity will you be listening? As Miss Hale the counsellor, dispassionate and cool, or as Jemma, the girl with warmth and laughter in her eyes and a mouth that says "kiss me if you can"?'

'I think,' with a firm smile, she eased away, 'I must put a distance between us for the moment.' He made as if to pull her back but changed his mind. 'You invited me here to talk to me, to tell me your problems. If I——' she looked away because his eyes were too dangerous to meet, 'if I——' She ran her tongue around her lips. 'If I arouse your desires, activate your male reflexes, well, I'm sorry about that, but——'

'Don't be.' He spoke abruptly. 'Let's eat.' He led the way, saying over his shoulder, 'The food's in the breakfast-room. We'd be lost at the dining-table. Nothing hot. Do you mind?'

Jemma was shaking her head when Arne opened the door to a small room which, decoratively speaking, was restrained when compared with the rest of the house. The table was covered with dishes of savouries and salads. 'All provided as a labour of love by my lady housekeeper, Mrs Wirral. Self-service.' He indicated plates and cutlery.

They sat on a balustraded terrace, resting their plates on a low table. The view across the Berkshire Downs was a delight, the sun beginning its downward journey and casting shadows across the distant fields.

As they ate, he asked, 'Do you like my house?'

'It's fantastic. And its contents.'

He let a few mouthfuls go down before he enquired casually, 'If it were yours, Jemma, how would you change it?'

'That's an academic question. It will never be mine.' She stared at the view, wondering why there was a tight knot in the centre of her chest. Sharing a house—a life?— with this man would, she had to admit it now, be nothing short of heaven. 'Second,' she glanced over her shoulder and into the dining-room behind them, 'I don't think I'd want to alter a single thing.'

'The masks, the tribal sculpture, the wooden gods? You'd leave them where they are?'

She laughed, her eyes sparkling. 'I wouldn't dare touch them. They might start talking and putting me in my place, telling me to get back into my own crazy modern world and leave them to their primitive peace!'

He smiled. 'So you wouldn't want to make alterations and sweeping changes? You wouldn't want to imprint your own personality on the place, regardless?'

Putting down her plate, she looked at him askance. 'I get the impression that someone—a woman, I'd guess—has trodden on your toes in that respect? Vowing she'd alter everything within reach; and now you're testing me to get another woman's viewpoint?'

'A neat piece of analysis, Jemma.' He put his plate down, too, but decisively. He's closed up on me, she thought unhappily.

The first barrier of the evening had come down and she shivered involuntarily.

Arne frowned. 'It gets cold out here in the evenings.' He held out his hand. 'We'll take our coffee in the living-room.'

Her hand lay in his and he studied it, a slight smile curving his lips. It came from that invisible side of him which held itself so tantalisingly aloof from contact with the everyday world; the side that Jemma longed to reach.

Hand in hand, they went inside, but she tried to break free. 'The dishes, I'll collect them and take them to the kitchen.'

'They'll be OK until Mrs Wirral finds them in the morning.' Arne looked down at her. 'Sometimes,' he said softly, 'it's possible to be too conscientious.'

'If you knew me better, you'd realise you're wasting your breath saying that, because that's how I'm made.'

She thought he said, 'It's something I intend to do,' but the words were lost in the bubbling of the coffee-machine standing on the table. Do what? she wondered.

He means, she answered herself, that in asking my advice he believes he'll learn more about the way my mind works. But he won't, because the part of my brain that advises professionally doesn't touch my emotions, and in a woman it's surely the emotions that form the basis of her personality.

Their coffee-cups stood empty, and Jemma gathered them for something to do. Her hands were restless, having picked up the tossing and turning of her mind at the thought of the advisory session to come.

'Let me have them,' Arne said, taking the crockery from her. 'Your fastidious habits must be seen to be believed.'

'I won't apologise for them,' she responded, smiling, 'since they're part of my make-up. So take them or leave them.'

'I'll take them,' he answered softly. 'Oh, yes, I'll take them.' He made a move towards her, remembered the objects in his hands and uttered a mild curse, removing them to the kitchen.

Jemma stared out at the darkening landscape, the shadowy trees receding into the parkland and the descending night. The wall lights were switched on and hands turned her by the shoulders.

'What's wrong?'

You, she wanted to tell him, you and your problem woman. It had to be that, she told herself again. Hadn't he started to tell her about it that evening he had taken her for a drink? 'I've fallen impossibly in love,' he had started to tell her. 'Impossible' was the giveaway word, the reason for his need of her advice.

How could she give it with the impartiality and detachedness his trust in her deserved? When the merest brushing of his hand against her skin caused runnels of desire to race through her, the whisper of his breath made her want to lift her mouth for his kisses?

'Nothing's wrong,' she answered.

'Now that is difficult to believe.' He bent his head to kiss her, but she turned her face aside. His eyebrows lifted and he moved. 'If it's my problem that's preying on your mind, we'll talk it out.'

A powerful grip propelled her to the sofa and he joined her, his hand slipping down to hold her wrist as if he anticipated a move on her part to put a distance between them.

It was nevertheless just such a distance that she did manage to impose. Putting her knees discreetly together and holding her back straight against the natural pull of the settee, she turned to him. 'What's your problem?'

His amusement at her behaviour made her face turn pink, but she would not allow herself to relax. With her body tautened, she told herself that she was in a better state of readiness to withstand the mention of the name of the woman about whom he intended consulting her.

He glanced at her clasped hands, her rich brown hair, then at the cool light of impartiality in her eyes. He lifted his hands to clasp them behind his head and raised a foot to rest his ankle on his opposite thigh.

'You possess understanding. That much I've learned about you. Compassion, too.'

Jemma waited, her patience strained to its limit.

'Also, you're objective in your professional approach?' This time it was truly a question.

'Yes.' The word was cut off, her reaction less certain.

'Then advise me.'

Jemma stared down at her hands. There was a tense silence. Then it came from out of the blue.

'I want to break free, to live life in my own way.'

Jemma was stunned, but nodded expressionlessly, head poised at a listening angle. Her eyes refused to meet his, signalling her deep interest as they usually did to people asking her advice. Instead, they kept their increasing fear to themselves.

'I want, Jemma, to resign from my job. Would you approve of such a step?'

She did not answer, since the idea appalled her so. Looking about her, she could see how disastrous such a step would be financially.

'Would you go along, Jemma,' he leaned forward, clasped hands suspended loosely between his thighs, 'with the idea of a man who, having reaching the position in the world of business that I have, wished with all his heart to let his life take its own course, instead of having his every move during working hours, and even those beyond them, decided for him?'

'With—with all his heart, you said?' She was speaking to her hands.

'I did.'

'There would be worries about being unemployed.' She looked around again at the quality of his possessions, his expensive taste in material things. 'Your standard of living couldn't possibly remain as high as it is now with no job to bring in money.'

'But I wouldn't be unemployed.'

'So you'd be working—at something you wanted to do, rather than being compelled to do, by the dictates of your job. I understand that. What I meant was, would the money you'd be earning bear any comparison with the salary you get now?' She waited for a moment for his response, which did not come. 'And if not,' her eyes swung to him, experiencing a shock from the electrifying brightness of his gaze, 'would you perhaps feel it beneath your dignity to line up, collecting unemployment benefit?'

'Do you ask all your advice-seeking clients this?'

Her gaze glittered at his challenge. 'I do, if I consider it appropriate, and I believe it to be so now. Sometimes,

I have to shock people into realising just what they'd be doing. I'm trying to bring home to *you* the cataclysmic effect your resignation from your highly paid job would have on your entire way of life.'

There was a veiled anger in his answering look, but he responded with a shrug. 'Fair enough.'

The strained silence that followed made Jemma want to plead: Say something. A glance told her, however, that Arne was thoughtful rather than tense.

He said at last, 'You don't approve, do you, of what I'm telling you. Reared to conformity, as you've obviously been, you wouldn't understand a man's craving to pull up anchor and go with the tide.'

Her eyes clouded at the way he was talking, denigrating her ability to perceive and go along with challenge.

'I understand,' she said quietly, 'much more than you give me credit for.'

'Where young people are concerned, maybe,' he conceded, 'but where an older person is concerned, one who's reached the apex of his career——'

'As you have,' she interrupted, nodding. 'Yes, even you, even your longings and aspirations, I think I understand.'

'So you'd approve,' he pressed, 'if I resigned from my safe, salaried position, cutting loose from convention and conformity?'

Jemma felt like weeping, wanting to tell him: But then I'd never see you again, never walk the corridors at work wondering if we might pass each other and smile...

'Do you really want my advice?' Since he did not say 'no', she asked, staring at the antique embroidered fire-screen which hid the unused grate.

'Yes, I do.'

She took a deep breath. 'If, as you said, you wish with all your heart that you could break free from your present way of life, from its set pattern, then——' She hesitated, asking herself what right she had to be giving advice to this man—and such advice! But he had asked her, hadn't he? In all seriousness, he had asked her.

'Then?' He stood squarely in front of her.

Agitatedly, she shook her head. She had to close her eyes tightly to trap the tell-tale tears. What she was about to say was as good as telling him to go out of her life. Fingers lifted her face, male lips prompted, 'Then——?'

'Then do it, leave your job, go your own way.' She took a breath. 'If you're sure you have the courage, the ability to adapt to a lower standard of living—and I think that you do—then go ahead. Pull up anchor and go where the tide takes you. We——' she moistened her lips, 'we all of us have only one life to live.'

The fingers under her chin tightened. 'Look at me, Jemma.' Reluctantly, she complied. 'This advice you've just given me—it's your honest opinion?'

'My honest opinion.'

'You knew exactly what you were doing in advising me to take that course?' She nodded. 'You've just told me to leave a well-paid, respected position in an equally respected company. Think hard. Now tell me you were completely aware of what you were saying.'

'I was completely aware,' she answered firmly. 'I meant every word, Arne. Take my advice or leave it, as you wish.'

His hand grasped her wrist, forcing her to unclench her fingers. He pulled her up. 'I take it, Jemma.' She was in his arms, his face in her hair, his trailing mouth against her throat, on her lips. 'I take your advice. Now, Jemma, my sincere and honest Jemma, will you marry me?'

CHAPTER FOUR

THE shock of his proposal was so strong that she shuddered in his arms. He pressed her against him as a way of calming her down, but its effect was exactly the opposite. Her heartbeats picked up the racing rhythm of his, and she raised her head from his shoulder where it had been lying.

'I'm not sure I understand,' she whispered. 'Is this where all your questioning was leading? You were really testing my reaction?'

He searched her face. 'Maybe I was. If so, I had my reasons.'

'Some other woman you'd proposed to,' she probed, 'she turned you down when you put the proposal to her? That—that woman,' she added dully, 'being Johanna.'

He did not say 'no'.

A sigh was torn from her. She loved him, she would have loved to have married him and become this man's wife, his lover. But she could not live out her life with him knowing she was merely a substitute for the woman he had really wanted to marry.

'I'm sorry,' she answered, her voice low. 'Thank you, all the same, for asking me.'

'There's someone else?' he shot at her harshly.

'There's no one else now, I told you that.'

'So?' He was becoming angry.

What could she say—'I won't be second-best woman in any man's life, especially yours'?

58

His jaw thrust forward, his eyes burned, searing a path to the very heart of her. He gripped her arm, his fingers compressing her flesh. 'So why have you turned my proposal down? Are you appalled now by the picture of me, having taken your advice, lounging around and lazing my days away? Couldn't you stand being tied to a husband who had voluntarily made himself unemployed, then had to line up for handouts from the State?'

If she shook her head, meaning, 'You're wrong in your assumption', he would take it as indicating that it was true that the thought of taking on such a partner horrified her. So she willed herself not to move.

'Will you answer me, Jemma, will you be honest and tell me that I've hit on the truth? That your compassion and sympathy, warm-heartedness and understanding are merely a professional veneer, and that deep down you're as prejudiced against the less fortunate in society as many other people are?'

'You're insulting me,' she flared, 'hurting me so deeply you make me feel ill. How could you misjudge me like that? Refusing your offer of marriage has absolutely nothing to do with your position in life, either now or in whatever future you choose for yourself.'

'So——' he took a ragged breath, 'so I withdraw my accusations, but only on condition that you tell me the real reason for your refusal. Jemma,' he cupped her face and stared into her eyes, 'I know you care. Your eyes are a giveaway, every time you look at me.'

Her lips were trembling with the words 'It's true I love you', when she remembered the rumour. Johanna, it had said, had been on the point of marriage to Arne, when completely unexpectedly she had become the wife of Arne's colleague, David Forrest. Which must surely confirm that the woman who had rejected him had indeed been Johanna Forrest.

'Will you take me home?' She had managed to control her tremulous lips.

Those eyes of his, those all-seeing brilliant eyes, blazed with a fiery anger, then they dimmed and Jemma felt icy cold as their fire went out.

The journey back was dark and silent. When the car drew up at the kerb, Jemma moved her hand towards the door, only to discover that she was too distressed to find the catch. Keeping her head turned away, she remained still, hoping that Arne would think that she was waiting for him to be polite and come round to open it for her.

Instead, he said coldly, 'You're home, which is where you wanted to be.'

A series of sobs racked her and she reached out blindly, feeling a piece of metal that gave. The door swung open. She was half-way to freedom when his hand pulled her back.

'What's wrong with you?' he rapped out. 'Realising that what I said about you is true—that the idea of taking to yourself a semi-impoverished, unemployed husband horrifies you?'

In the car's interior light, he saw her face. 'My God, why didn't you tell me?'

He pulled her across and his cheek was dampened by the tears which had come so silently. He released her, getting out and going swiftly round the car as she rubbed at her face with the pads of her fingers.

He made a 'come on out' movement with his head. She complied, walking slowly towards the entrance doors. Locking the car, he followed, his arm lightly holding hers. In the lift, they stood apart while, under his narrow-eyed scrutiny, she searched in her bag for the key.

He took it as they neared the door, using it and going in after her. As she switched on the living-room light, he took her into his arms.

'Am I the cause of those tears?' She nodded, bending her head and placing her overheated forehead against his chest. 'Tell me why you said "no", Jemma.' His voice was low, coaxing an answer.

He moved, and she felt her skin prickle as his fingers parted the hair at her nape. His lips were swift to follow and her nerves stung as if his touch was electrically charged. Her hands gripped his shoulders, loving their strength.

'Tell me,' he urged again, pushing the neck of her dress aside and teasing her flesh with his tongue.

'When you asked me to marry you and I said "no", I was lying.' Her head tilted and she sought those incredible eyes of his. 'I do want to marry you. I can't help myself. I love you,' she whispered against his mouth, 'I love you so much I can't put my feelings for you into words.'

'Jemma, my Jemma.' He gathered her to him and his kiss held such passion and feeling her doubts died away. Until her exasperating, questioning brain reminded her, What about the woman he told you he was in love with?

To avoid the irresistible trap of his eyes, she scratched with her fingers through the button fastening of his shirt. 'That evening you took me for a drink, Arne, you mentioned a woman. You were in love with her, you said. You wanted my opinion——'

'You've given it to me, Jemma.' He held her away. 'You are the woman I was talking about. *My beautiful, compassionate woman.* Remember?'

'When you said that,' she exclaimed, 'you weren't talking about Johanna, you were talking about *me*?'

'Johanna?' His voice was filled with distaste. 'I don't play around with married women.'

'Which meant,' her eyes opened with near-disbelief, 'you were in love with *me*?'

'Was, am and forever will be.'

He spoke the words as if they were a pledge and her parted lips received his kiss, returning it and receiving yet more until she was drunk with them. Her heart soared with an unbelievable happiness, as it rejoiced in the fact that cold reason had taken her down the wrong road.

Of course she was not second-best to Johanna Forrest. It was she, Jemma, he loved, he had told her so, and with such passion she just had to believe him. He had put Johanna and his past relationship with her behind him.

Hadn't he?

Early next morning, he returned. Jemma had given him the key. Sunday stretched luxuriously before her and she slept on beyond her normal time of waking and rising.

The night before, he had left her reluctantly, holding her as if she were something precious and telling her that in a few days they would be man and wife.

'Let's wait to make love, Arne. Please,' she had said.

'What's a few days, darling, in a lifetime?'

'A lifetime,' he groaned, gathering her to him again, 'but if that's what you want, I'll agree, although it's tearing me apart to leave you.'

Now he was back, and he stood watching her sleeping. The cover was half-way down her body, her delicate nightdress slipping low enough to reveal most of her breasts. He sat on the bed and lowered his mouth to touch the soft flesh.

Wakened by the feathering of his lips, leaping to full, shivering consciousness by his roving mouth which was making the hardened pink peaks his own, Jemma's arms flung themselves around him and drew him down beside her.

He had discarded his sweater. It lay on a chair on top of her underwear. It looked, she thought, bemused, as though the owners of those clothes were already man and wife. *As though he belonged.* It was her dream come true!

He kicked off his shoes as her fingers fumbled with his shirt buttons. He helped her, shaking free of the garment.

For the first time, she saw the warm, strong masculinity of him, the muscled breadth of his body, the flesh that felt taut and sinewy and held his own special scent.

'Arne,' her smile told him of her happiness, 'I think you're the most wonderful man I've ever met.'

'And you've known so many,' he teased.

She laughed and traced a path through the miniature jungle of his chest hair. 'The first time I saw you I think I knew. Yet, isn't it strange, I knew so little about you, then—and not very much more now!'

'We can spend our combined lifetimes learning each other's ways.'

She nestled against him. 'So tell your counsellor, darling,' she stole a glance upwards and encountered a roughened, as yet unshaven, jaw, 'what you intend to do with your life once you've resigned from your highly paid job.'

He kissed her impish smile, then settled her now-naked body against him. His arms were around her but his mind had turned in on itself. 'I intend to work as an artist.'

Jemma secretly closed her eyes, pressing down the lids. She had heard it all before in the course of her work— the urge to branch out into creativity, the desire for self-expression through painting, through music, acting or writing... all without the benefit of training, but motivated every time by a deep, unexpressed yearning to escape from reality and discover and express the inner self. And always, too, with the certainty of eventual recognition, of success to come, and naturally, the financial rewards that would go with that success.

'Sculpting is my line,' he was saying.

What can I do, she thought, but give my support and encouragement? 'Like the figures I saw in your house?'

'Right, Jemma,' he answered, his chin moving against her head. 'Some of those efforts are mine.'

His words gave her a jolt. They surely weren't bad! One-offs, she assured herself, pure fluke, but showing promise. She recalled the figure whose sex she had not been able to judge. The face had been a blur, the gender of the body unidentifiable. It had been the work of an amateur—which Arne was, of course. He had made no claims to be anything else. But that piece of work had somehow felt good, she recalled, in her hands. And somehow pleased her eyes, too, which surely meant he was gifted and would go places... One day...

'So you've got savings to see you through?'

He jerked up her chin. A frown had changed his face, momentarily frightening her. 'See *us* through,' he corrected. 'Yes, I've got savings, Jemma. When we're married, they'll be quite adequate for our needs.'

She nodded against him. 'And with the money I bring in from my job, we'll manage just fine, darling.'

He did not reply and she lay contentedly against him. 'Your counsellor's signing-off,' she said, her smiling lips moving against him. He stirred.

'Jemma,' his voice was strained, 'I want you, here and now I want you. OK, so we ageed to wait, but——'

'Oh, *please* let's wait, Arne. I love you more than life itself and I want you as much as you want me, but——' she distanced herself a little, 'I have to tell you. I've taken no precautions.'

'A few days, what does it matter. Tomorrow I'll get a licence. If a child's conceived——'

'No!' It had almost been a cry of pain. He looked at her, shock and the faintest hint of anger mingling.

'You don't want children?' He spoke so coldly he had almost turned into a stranger.

'Of course I do, I love children, but——'

'Other people's?'

'One day, I shall love *our* children more than anything in the world. But not yet, Arne, not yet.'

He moved from her entangling arms and Jemma felt the cold air plunge between them. Looking down, she became truly conscious of her naked state and drew the cover over her.

'I remember now,' he said, and it was as if he were speaking from a million miles away. 'We've been here before, haven't we? Your future's planned to the last detail. Jemma Hale's career comes first and last.'

'I had my training, Arne. My parents struggled to finance my studies. I can't throw it all away.' Her voice was taut and thick with strain. 'I like my job too much to put it all behind me. Helping people——'

'Which doesn't include your husband.'

Jemma was silent, closing her eyes and breathing shallowly in case she lost control over the threatening tears. 'It's over, isn't it, before it's even begun. I'm sorry, Arne. I—I love you so very much, but we see things so differently, it isn't really possible for us to go on together, is it?'

He had swung from the bed, still partially clothed, and was staring over the rooftops to the countryside beyond.

'I'm thirty-four, Jemma. I want children. I see other men with their wives, their *families*. I love other people's kids. I want some of my own.'

Jemma's lips trembled, her body shook silently.

'I want those children by the woman I love most in the world.' He swung round. 'You.'

Her tears tasted salty on her dry lips. What should she do? All her training had not taught her the answer to this. All you people who come to see me, she thought, to get my advice, what would you say if you knew that the woman who advised you could not solve her own problems?

There was such a long pause, Jemma thought it really was all over; that any moment he would pull on his shirt, toss her the door key and go.

'Jemma,' his voice sounded tortured, 'I'm so in love with you, I'm willing to let you have your way. We'll wait for the family. You can have your career.'

She flung from the bed and pulled him into her arms, kissing his shoulders, his neck and pressing her mouth with abandon into his.

'But Jemma,' he said in a cracked voice, 'don't make me wait too long.'

'I promise, my darling, not long, not too long...' She wanted him now with an overpowering need. 'Arne, let's make love. Now, here and now. Please, Arne.'

He gave a harsh-sounding laugh, pushing her arms from him. 'Isn't that woman-like?' he joked, but his voice was tense. 'No child yet, she pleads, but let's make love regardless. No barrier to the conception of the next generation, she says, but let's take the risk and go ahead... although, and I quote you, *I don't want children yet.*' He was amused and exasperated and irritated all at once. 'No, no. We'll wait, do you hear? So cover yourself up,' he exclaimed angrily. 'It's driving me mad to see the beauty of you, yet have to force my hands to stay at my sides.'

A strained smile softened his rigid jawline. 'My God——' he seized her, despite his words, swinging her in a circle until her legs lifted, then put her down and placed his mouth against hers, pushing into its inner recesses, plunging, savouring, until her head fell back—it was as if he were taking possession of her that way 'the taste of you, the feel of you! I——'

He put her from him, lifting shaking hands to smooth his hair where her fingers had run through it and clung. 'I'm going away for a few days. Business, to Italy. It's just as well.' His mouth twisted slightly. 'Otherwise, that child you don't want might be thrust upon you and you'd hate me ever after for depriving you of that career you love so much.'

'Oh, Arne, don't be bitter. We'll have children, of course we will. One day.'

He stood before her, legs astride, fists on hips. 'Which of us is going to decide the time and place? Which of us will say to the other, Now we'll make love, this time going all out to start that tiny new life on its way?'

Jemma shook her head helplessly. 'There's no need to look at it like that. It will happen one day, spontaneously.'

'*One day*. Is that all you can find to say? Let's make an appointment in your overflowing diary. ''Start a family.'' ' It was a sneer and Jemma despaired.

'Arne,' she said shakily, 'I think you'll have to look for another woman to marry. Our approach to life is almost incompatible. Our priorities couldn't be more different.'

The telephone thrust a misplaced trill into the brittle atmosphere. Pulling a sheet around her, Jemma twisted to answer it. 'Yes?' Oh, not Richard! she thought. Her fingers pressed into her cheek. She listened, then closed her eyes. 'Yes, I meant it and—you must be honest with yourself—you did, too. We just came to the end of our particular round, didn't we.' She listened again. 'Bye, Richard. It's been nice knowing you, too.'

Two arms came round her and a roughened cheek rubbed against hers. Replacing the receiver, she turned slowly into Arne's arms and the tears came, then—reaction to her quarrel with Arne, to her uncertainty as to whether she was doing right in wanting to stay in her job; the tug inside of the child she was intending to deny the man she loved so deeply, when he wanted it so much.

'He's achieved something,' Arne conceded softly. 'He's pushed you off that ridiculous fence you were sitting on and down into my arms. And,' he added, pressing his lips against her hair, 'into the rest of my life.'

There was a prolonged silence, then, as if tried beyond endurance, he wrapped his arms about her. 'To hell with priorities,' he exclaimed. 'Love's the vital bridge between couples. Let's concentrate on that, shall we?'

He kissed each eye, then her mouth with infinite tenderness. 'Now, my love,' he held her away, looking her over, 'I want to meet those parents of yours.'

She scratched his unshaven cheek with her nail. 'Suppose they don't approve?'

'Of me?' His eyebrow lifted quizzically. 'You think they won't?'

Her arms crept round his neck. 'They'll love you, just as I do.'

'Hm. They'd better,' he replied in mock threat, then kissed her until she gasped for mercy.

While she dressed, Arne left her. He wouldn't, he said, be able to stand there watching her without breaking his good resolution and making passionate love to her.

As she joined him in the living-room, he lowered the magazine he had been reading and looked at her with passion in his eyes.

She had dressed with care, both to please him and because she would be presenting him to her parents out of the blue as her husband-to-be. Her ruby-red, long-sleeved crepe dress was one of her mother's favourites.

Not that she anticipated opposition from her mother. On the contrary, she was sure that both her parents would be delighted with her choice of husband. Broad-minded and tolerant as they were, she knew they would even understand when they heard about Arne's intentions where his life's work was concerned.

He stood swiftly, going to her and taking her into his arms, kissing her and finding her breasts, holding them possessively.

'I'll be away for three days,' he said thickly. 'The day after my return, we'll be married. I refuse to wait any longer.'

'Thursday?' Jemma calculated. 'It's a weekday. I've got appointments——'

'Postpone them.' There was authority in his voice as well as irritation. He was, after all, still one of the top men at Prospect Industrial. 'It will be Thursday.' He looked her over, the message in his eyes unmistakable. 'Or now. A man has only so much patience. The choice, Jemma, is yours.'

'Thursday, Arne.' She was coming to realise that this man could be pushed so far, but beyond that ... She dared not speculate. 'I'll have to give everyone fresh appointments.'

'You'll have to learn to say "no",' he smiled, 'to them as well as to me.'

'Oh, Arne,' she went to him and put her arms round his neck, 'it'll be fun, and it'll be a challenge. We'll have a happy marriage, darling, and you'll reach your goal, I'm sure of it.'

She tugged at his shoulders, putting up her face for his kiss. His arms came round her and she was engulfed in his embrace.

The zip-fastener at the back of her dress gave and the shoulders were pushed aside by impatient hands. His lips touched her prickling skin, her throat, her shoulders and, as the dress dropped lower, the soft curves of her breasts. Her hands rubbed softly round the back of his neck and down his shoulders as the movement of his mouth upon her hardened breasts made her breath catch in her throat and her eyes close in near-ecstasy.

He made an enormous effort to tame his desires, lifting his head and drawing her dress back into place. 'If we weren't going out, and I weren't about to meet my future in-laws, I'd have taken you here and now, regardless of the consequences.' He let out a short-tempered breath.

'How many hours to our wedding?' He looked into her bright gaze and groaned. 'If I hadn't got these appointments abroad over the next few days, we could have said to hell with waiting...'

'You know why we agreed to hold back,' she reminded him softly.

For a moment, the blue depths of his eyes grew stormy, then he let her go. 'My memory's not that short.'

Again it hit her that, by her attitude, she was hurting the man she loved above everyone else. Was she being selfish, she agonised, in wanting to stay in her job? She enjoyed it so much. Was it wise to marry this man who plainly would have preferred her to give up everything and have the child he wanted so much? But she had to marry him, she couldn't help herself. She couldn't let him go.

'Arne,' the soft pads of her fingers slid over his face, 'do you realise you'll be marrying an artistic illiterate?'

'You're much too hard on yourself,' he admonished her. 'And don't worry, I'll teach you everything you need to know, especially how to appreciate your husband's work! Tell me,' more seriously, 'what does colour mean to you?'

'In life? I love colours. It may sound ingenuous and sentimental, but the sunrise and sunset—they really move me.'

'It's a start, Jemma,' he answered quietly, pulling her to him again. 'It lifts you, visually speaking, way above most other people who don't even seem to know that the sun, apart from browning their skin while they're on vacation, sheds any colours over the earth at all!'

CHAPTER FIVE

FOR a few moments, Jemma stood alone, admiring her new husband from afar with something near to adoration in her eyes.

That tall, lean man across the room, she tried telling herself for the twentieth time, had just been through the marriage ceremony with her and they were now bound until death them did part.

What if an insistent voice kept trying to say, 'You should have waited a while, got to know each other better...Jemma Hale, you're a foolish, hot-headed'— except that she was Jemma Drummond now and she had no regrets of any kind.

'I hope you'll be very happy,' Dave Forrest broke into her thoughts. 'If my wife Johanna had been able to get here in time, I'm sure she would have joined me in wishing you every happiness.'

'Thanks for that,' Jemma answered, smiling even as she doubted the good wishes he was offering on behalf of his missing wife.

During the wedding reception he had watched from the edge of the crowd, refusing to be drawn into any of the photographs, official or otherwise.

Jemma was struck once again by the man's detachment, his total lack of emotion. Either that, she reasoned, or he kept all his feelings battened down. He had not smiled, even when wishing her well, his grey eyes empty, his good features, topped by a shock of red-brown hair, somehow not quite adding up to handsomeness.

Dave drifted to a neighbouring group. Alone again, Jemma looked around for her husband—strange and mysterious word, she thought with a smile of self-mockery. It hadn't yet ceased to astonish her how quickly the wedding arrangements had been made.

In four days, her delighted parents had risen magnificently to the occasion. In four days, with help provided by Prospect Industrial's willing staff, the ceremony had been applied for, the licence obtained and the reception hall booked.

Arne appeared as if her thoughts had summoned him. His arm pulled her to his side and the happiness in his face made his colleague, who had turned at that moment, look more deadpan than ever. He made his way towards them.

'Hi, Dave,' Arne said. 'You've met my wife, of course.' He glanced down into Jemma's startled face at his description of her. It hadn't sunk in yet, her change of status. When it had, she knew she would reel at the speed with which her life had changed.

Dave Forrest joined them. 'I've wished Jemma well, Arne,' Dave said in his low-profile way, 'so I'll wish you all the best, too. How did your Italian visit go? Did you do any business?'

'Made a few sales, yes. I'll tell you about them some time. When my brain reverts to its normal functioning.'

He held Jemma's eyes and she his. Dave, plainly feeling like a left-over at a wedding feast, wandered away. Someone called Arne's name. He pressed a kiss against Jemma's forehead and promised to return in a few minutes.

Cindy called to Jemma, waving madly, her face alight with a happiness that could not have been entirely due to attending the 'fairy-tale' wedding, as she had called it, of her boss. Beside her was a tall, fair young man whom Jemma recognised as being the subject of the photograph on Cindy's desk.

Arne's voice, raised in laughter, came from the centre of a group of colleagues. Her pulse-rate accelerated at the tall and handsome sight of him. His face was filled with a happiness which, she marvelled, could only be there because he had married her, Jemma Hale.

As she made her way to his side, a sinuous, feline kind of movement wove its way into her side vision. A slender, golden-haired woman floated into her path, halting her. The woman's looks were flawless, the make-up superfluous since the beautiful features would have been fascinating without any cosmetic enhancement.

There was no pleasure in the woman's gaze on approaching the bride, no good wishes hovering on her lips. There was instead a barely veiled malevolence.

Jemma's smile, however, was as determinedly steady as her gaze. 'You made it after all, Mrs Forrest,' she exclaimed, simulating pleasure. 'I'm so glad, and Arne will be, too.'

Johanna looked Jemma over, her flashing emerald eyes appraising and reluctantly acknowledging the good taste and cut of Jemma's cream-shaded dress with its insets of hand-made lace and its simple, flowing lines.

'Don't speak for Arne,' Johanna Drummond said in a low, intense voice. 'What do *you* know about his fine mind, his most intimate thoughts? What do you know about him at all? How long have you known him?'

'Long enough, Mrs Forrest,' Jemma said with dignity, 'to know I'd met the one man in the world I wanted to live with for the rest of my life.' Jemma was proud of the way her voice held its strength and sureness. This woman would never be allowed to guess how her words were raising doubts like dust in a winter gale.

'Arne's a near-genius, did you know that?' Johanna persisted, her perfect mouth curved into a sneer. 'Of course you didn't. To you he's a closed book. It's only to me that he's opened up his mind, shared his thoughts and visions. *Me, not you!*'

Jemma almost rocked on her feet as each of Johanna's statements found its mark.

'He rushed you into this marriage, didn't he,' Johanna went on unmercifully. 'And I know darned well,' she looked Jemma over, 'it's not because of the usual slightly sordid reason. He's too careful to have allowed that to happen.'

'All right,' Jemma challenged, dropping all pretence at friendliness, 'so tell me why he did marry me? As you say, there was no pressure on him to do so.' Her hands had started to shake and she gripped her bag to hide her agitation.

'He wanted a wife,' Johanna sneered. 'It was as simple as that. He told me once that every man should have one. A good hostess, he said, with a good appearance, those were the things he wanted in a wife. Good looks weren't essential, he said, but they'd be a bonus. Someone who'd be a healthy, sensible mother of his children. They were all that mattered, really, he told me.'

Her cheeks were flushed an angry pink. 'If his wife hadn't got the necessary——' her eyes flashed between Jemma and herself, and it was no mystery which of them came out better from that comparison, 'female enticements, he could always take a mistress—secretly and discreetly, of course.'

Jemma closed her eyes on a feeling of nausea. Johanna saw it and smiled. 'I'm sure,' Jemma got out, 'you more than meet Arne's requirements in all those respects. So why didn't he marry you?'

'It was the "mother of his children" angle that disqualified me, not because he'd stopped loving me or I'd stopped loving him.' Her green eyes were filled with hatred, her finely shaped mouth becoming a thin, blood-red line. 'I told him I hadn't any plans to produce offspring. And if he married me and tried to force them on me, I'd leave him——' Her lips reappeared and formed a ravishing curve. 'Didn't I, Arne, darling?'

He had come to stand beside Jemma, eyeing Johanna with a face so expressionless it might have been a mask.

Johanna's hand moved to rest on Arne's arm, her eyes shining into his as if someone had switched on an artificial sun in their depths. Then her husband called to her, having just discovered that she had arrived. She shone another ravishing smile into Arne's eyes and joined him.

Goaded by the woman's words, Jemma felt the anger she had been holding back smash through the dam. 'Well, did she?' Jemma thrust at Arne. 'Why don't you answer?' She wanted to shake him for his silence, for his refusal to deny Johanna's allegations. She swung away and the arm he had placed across her shoulders tightened to bring her back.

'What's Johanna been saying?' he demanded, the liquid blue of his eyes darkening dangerously.

'If you must know, she——' Jemma compressed her lips. How could she repeat Johanna's poisonous words? What if he said they were true? She wouldn't be able to stand it.

'She said——' Jemma's voice thickened, then she snapped her lips shut. She was quarrelling with her new husband...about another woman...in front of all their guests—*and on their wedding day!*

She had to get away. Anywhere would do.

'Leaving us, you two?' a friend of Arne's called out, watching Jemma making for the door. 'Hey, everybody, the bride and groom are on their way. Let's wave them off. Where's the confetti?'

Arne was beside her now and it was snowing coloured specks of paper, raining rice over hair and clothes and faces. Arms came round her, Cindy's, then her mother's.

'Your dad and I will take care of all the presents,' Brenda Hale whispered, 'until you and Arne are ready to take them.'

In the driving-seat, Arne ducked to avoid a handful of confetti. It missed him and floated all over Jemma. The car moved forward, leaving behind the good wishes and the madly waving arms.

As they gathered speed, Jemma realised how low her spirits had sunk. Thanks to Johanna, all her happiness and her hopes for the future, she felt, were part of the past now.

The timing of Johanna's arrival, Jemma thought bitterly, couldn't really be faulted. Almost too late to join in the festivities, but just in time to make certain that, when the bride and groom shared their marriage bed that night she, Johanna, would in spirit join them there, making it a ghostly threesome.

It was late afternoon when they checked into the hotel. On the way, Arne had made tight-lipped conversation to Jemma's monosyllabic replies. He had filled the tight silence with taped music.

The hotel grounds sloped down to meet the river and Jemma stood alone on the small balcony, watching the rippling flow lap against the banks. The mallards moving busily by reminded her of the evening Arne had taken her for a drink at the riverside pub.

The words he had spoken then had a hollow ring about them now. 'I've fallen impossibly in love,' he'd told her, 'with a beautiful woman...' 'Impossible' had been the vital word.

Johanna had been the obstacle to her happiness then, just as she was now. Her 'entrance' that particular evening had been as dramatic and disruptive to Jemma's peace of mind as her appearance at the wedding reception had been barely an hour ago.

Arne was testing the radio in the bedroom behind her, the discordant noises resolving at last into romantic and sensuous sound.

'Jemma?'

Her instinct was to turn and go to him. Instead, she forced herself to stay where she was. Arne's hands closed over her arms, but she tried to shake him off. A little more—his breath, say, on her cheek and she would throw herself into his arms. But Johanna was there, a dark shadow between them, her harsh voice still ringing in Jemma's ears.

Arne did not break contact, moving to stand beside her, his hand on her shoulder. He, too, surveyed the view, scanning the trees on the opposite bank, absently noting a walker waiting for his trailing dog. Downstream was a bridge; upstream, small boats were moored, bobbing on the restless ripples.

The music from the radio was beginning to work its magic, soothing Jemma's taut nerves. To her dismay, she discovered that it was filling her eyes and making her mouth tremble.

'You're miles away from me, Jemma,' Arne said huskily. 'I want you close.'

Couldn't he sense, Jemma thought desperately, that something was wrong? Couldn't he guess who was the cause? He pulled her towards him, but she fought free and, with Arne close behind her, pushed through into the room.

Puzzled, and with difficulty keeping his anger in check, Arne looked at her. Then he saw the tears and caught her against him, this time so close escape was impossible.

'This is ridiculous.' His cheek was against her hair. 'An hour ago, I looked across at you and you were treading cloud. Then came Johanna and you've been sending out hate messages towards me ever since. What did she say?'

'I'd have hardly thought it was necessary to tell you,' she said thickly. 'You must know it all by heart.' He did not answer, so she added, her voice muffled, 'I know now why you didn't marry her. I know now how *very well* you knew her. Mind and body...'

He let her go, slipping his hands into the pockets of his immaculate suit. His jaw showed its strength, his eyes had lost their brilliance and were as dark as a stormy sea. He was at that moment every inch the prosperous businessman, success in every line of him, the world his village.

Jemma fought with the feeling that this man she had married was a stranger, an enigma she despaired of ever solving, no matter how well she came to know him.

There was neither sight nor hint of the would-be artist, the amateur with creative ability inside him screaming to get out, if only his hand and eye were better trained to give it a fighting chance of success. How he would ever make the transformation from top-flight industrialist to struggling artist longing for recognition, Jemma did not know. *And she had been the one to encourage him to take such a step.* How would she ever forgive herself for such a terrible error of judgement, both personal and professional?

'I knew her well, as you say,' Arne followed up her statement evenly. 'In both body and mind. I'm no monk and she is very attractive. In fact, for a few short weeks, she wore my ring.'

Jemma's fingers spontaneously, and almost defensively, felt for the ring he had given *her*—a sparkling solitaire diamond. But she had something, hadn't she, that Johanna had never had—Arne's wedding ring nestling next to it?

'What I don't know,' Arne was saying, 'and you must tell me,' with sarcasm, 'since you now seem to be so much better informed on the subject than I am, is why I didn't marry her.'

'She wouldn't have your children,' she flung at him across the yawning chasm whose edges had opened gapingly between them.

'I can't deny that she refused to have children.' He was so reasonable, Jemma could have screamed. 'Nor can I deny that that particular subject reared its unpleasant head in the eventual break-up.' His mouth twisted a little. 'What other gratifying comments did she make about me?'

'That you'd opened up your mind to her and discussed your thoughts, your—your visions, she called them.'

'We certainly discussed my possible resignation from my job, plus my hopes for the future in the line I'd chosen to follow. Perfectly normal and acceptable subjects for a man to talk about with his fiancée.'

'There were other things, too.' Things that had to be said, she told herself, to be brought out into the open—the poisonous comments that Johanna had made. Wasn't it her own philosophy while counselling others?

He was removing his jacket now, behaving like a husband, a lover, distracting her with his breadth of shoulders under his silk shirt, his body's leanness. His hands were at his tie, loosening it, taking it off and un-buttoning his shirt collar, the spread of chest hair appearing. All the time, his eyes were on her.

'Other things?' His shirt sleeves were being rolled up now, and she saw the layer of dark, fine hair on his arms. 'Such as?' His brows arched, he was the one now who was a million miles away.

She had to gather her wits, collect her thoughts which the sight of him had scattered. 'Your—your list of requirements in life. Every man, you said, should have a wife. Good looks in the woman would be a bonus...a good hostess...a healthy sensible mother of and to his children. And,' she finished tartly, 'if the woman you married for all these reasons was not enticing enough, or if she failed to satisfy your needs, you could always take a mistress.' The last few words nearly choked her.

He was in the small adjoining bathroom now, and she followed, standing at the door. He washed his face, dried his hands. Everyday acts but with an added familiarity which made Jemma realise just how small their knowledge was of each other and how short their acquaintance had really been. They weren't even lovers, they were strangers still and the thought made her curl up inside.

Had she made a terrible mistake? Events until now had carried her through, there had been no time to think, let alone to doubt. How little she knew about Arne Drummond. Even Johanna's comments, intended to goad, had thrown a light on a side of him she herself did not know.

If only they could have fallen straight into each other's arms and made love, free of inhibitions and restraint, the act itself would have forged an intimate link which would have bound them so closely, every bone and fibre of their being would have melded together, breaking through all barriers and making them one.

He looked fresh and clean, coming towards her, rolling down his sleeves and refastening his cuffs. 'So now you know why I married you. Is that what you're going to say.'

It was, but she could not bring herself to say it in case he admitted that it was true. He gave her a long, cool look and Jemma trembled a little inside. If he reached for her now, started to make controlled, deliberate love as his expression implied he had in mind, she would fight him all the way. He had said he loved her, but what man in love, just joined in marriage to the woman he professed to love, would look at her in such a hard, calculating way? Like a man assessing just how far he could go with a woman he had invited out for the evening.

'No message in those eyes of yours,' he said grimly. 'I'm damned if I'm going to make love to a woman who's quietly wishing me in hell.' He looked her over. 'Do whatever it is you want to do, then we'll dine.'

When she rejoined him half an hour later, he was still the archetypal businessman. Not even, she thought sadly, businessman at play. He sat, legs crossed, in a comfortable chair, leafing through magazines which had been left in a pile on a low glass-topped table. He had not changed out of his wedding suit, from which Jemma deduced that his body, like his mind, was refusing to relax.

If only he would, then she would have relaxed, too. Her limbs would have lost their tension, her mouth would have smiled, her eyes might even, despite the lingering poison of Johanna's claims, have whispered, 'Please love me.'

He liked her dress, there was no doubt about that. Putting aside the magazine, he stood up, openly eyeing her, admiring the way the blue and white patterned bodice, with its wrist-hugging sleeves and low-cut neckline followed her shape, while the skirt swung around her slender hips.

The trouble is, Jemma thought with sorrow, he doesn't seem to like *me* very much. I could smile, I could flash my eyes, I could even go up to him and put a kiss on his mouth—but I wouldn't be able to forget the stinging arrows which Johanna shot into me. Their acid was, even now, circulating in her body. So her voice, as deadpan as her face, told him, 'I'm ready.'

'Now that,' he commented cynically, 'I doubt. If I touched you, you'd scream like a frightened virgin.'

He was wrong about one thing, she thought with irony—her feelings towards him were anything but virginal!

'I meant,' she said with dignity—which was ridiculous since she was this man's wife—'I'm ready to go down to dinner.'

His expression unreadable, he opened the door and stood back, allowing her to pass, taking in every body movement she made.

He was, she thought, feeding his desire and his needs through the medium of his eyes. Where were they all going, those lustful feelings of his that were accumulating? And when the explosion finally came, would the eruption sweep her away—not only her emotions on a tide of passion, but her poisoned thoughts, too?

She could not have asked for a more romantic atmosphere. The low-beamed dining-room, hunting-prints around the walls, the soft red carpet, the candles flaring on every table—it was a perfect setting for a honeymoon couple deeply in love.

I thought we were, she cried inwardly, it was why we rushed into this marriage—couldn't wait, could we, to turn our cerebral love into sensual passion?

Crumbling her roll, she had to face the painful truth: that it was she, not Arne, who had erected the barrier. Yet, beyond that truth was another—that it was Johanna, not herself, who had laid the foundations, and the resentment had built, brick by brick, like a wall too tall to scale.

Throughout the meal, Arne talked; about the reception, the guests, about how strange it had been to be saying 'goodbye' to colleagues he had worked with for so long. And she responded, coaxing him to talk, using the 'counsellor' side of her personality to cross a mental bridge into his mind, while all the time something cried out inside her: 'We might just as well be sharing a business dinner, exchanging opinions, discussing work, plans for future expansion...'

Once, looking up, she caught an ironic gleam and it gave her a painful shock. It was like a light picking up a flitting shadow on a darkened stage. His thoughts, it told her, were anywhere but on their conversation.

She hadn't succeeded, had she, she hadn't achieved the goal she had set herself, of getting behind the front he showed to the world? She might now be his wife, wearing his ring—the plain gold band, the one that mattered. Yet his inner self was still as much a secret to her as it had been the day they had first met. *But not to Johanna.*

'Finished?' He was so polite it hurt. Pushing back his chair, he came round to help her rise from hers. Tall and handsome, he escorted her to the exit doors. She opted for climbing the stairs. Standing with him in the lift, with silence between them and his sardonic smile playing over her, would have been purgatory in miniature.

It wasn't much better when they reached their room. He removed his jacket, throwing it aside as if it weighed heavily on his shoulders. To Jemma, her senses crying out for contact with his, it was as if he were throwing away their marriage.

'So why did you marry me,' she heard herself cry out, 'if it wasn't just because I didn't refuse to have children and Johanna did?'

He turned from the window, tossing his tie to a chair. His mouth was taut, the blue of his eyes darkened with anger. 'I married you for the very good reason that I fell in love with you—*with you as you were*—a warm, compassionate woman.'

'But Arne, I haven't changed,' she cried passionately. 'How could I have?' Her eyes were moist, she couldn't clear them. 'What Johanna said upset me. Reverse the situation. Suppose an ex-fiancé of mine—not that there's been one—had come up to you at our wedding and said to you what *your* ex-fiancée said to me, implying that I still loved him...'

'I'd have strangled him.'

Her smile broke through, lighting up her face. 'Now do you see what I mean?'

'I see, yes, but I wouldn't have borne a grudge against you as you now seem to be doing against me.' She was shaking her head, but he went on, 'It's in the past, Jemma, all of it. This is *now*.' His voice was deep, vibrating with emotion. 'This is the future. Come, my love, will you share it with me?' His arms came out.

Blinking away her tears, she ran into them. They closed about her, pulling her to his hard body. He smiled down at her, and there was so much tenderness in his eyes that her heart turned over. Her mouth reached up, wanting his kiss, her hands gripped his head, pulling it down, her mouth putting itself against his.

The floodgates opened and his passion roared free. He took over the kiss, no longer gentle, nor restrained as he had been before the wedding, but rough and demanding, like his hands on her body.

She swayed under his fierce need, and the kiss held. He was unfastening her dress, baring her shoulders, kissing each newly revealed area of silky skin. His fingers deftly unhooked her lacy bra, then almost with reverence he lifted each breast, caressing it with his eyes before savouring it with his lips, his tongue, his teeth, drawing tiny gasps from her throat.

His hands found their way to her bare, throbbing flesh, first beneath her clothes, then discarding them one by one. When she was naked, his gaze encompassed her shape, appraising the hardened fullness of her breasts, the way her neat stomach rounded and her hips melted into her slender thighs. He was studying the essential femininity of her as if the artist in him were memorising every smallest dimple and shadowed-in line.

'One day, by God,' he muttered, 'I'll sculpt you.'

'Sculpt *me*, Arne?' she responded breathlessly.

'You of all women,' he responded, narrowing his eyes as they swept over her. 'How can I capture it, the essential *womanness* of you, that love, that tenderness in your expression? But right now,' he released her, pulling free of his own clothes and standing before her tall and proudly naked, his breadth and masculinity robbing her of breath, 'I want to take you into me, melt you down and blend you into my blood. Jemma, beloved,' holding her, he stroked her, breast, hip, thigh, 'it's been hell waiting. Then this evening you froze me out, talking to me as if we were strangers. You were killing me slowly, cut by cut——'

'No, no, Arne, you were doing that to *me*, keeping me at a distance,' she told him feverishly. 'You might as well have been on the moon.' She shivered and he enveloped her, and she responded to his hard male need, his heated loins warming her, arousing her unbearably.

He carried her to the bed, his mouth coming down wide and hungry over hers, pulling her lips into him, his tongue rough in its curling exploration of the moist, sweet cavities of her cheeks.

She tangled with him and he pushed his hand between her inner thighs, stroking them, creating fresh paths of tension and aching need. He was prolonging the moment of piercing desire, sweeping his palms upward until she arched and snaked under his caresses, her body opening to him, inviting him of its own accord.

When his invasion came, she gave to him her sweetly pulsing womanhood, her rapture soaring at each and every thrust of his total possession.

Together they climbed, on and on to the explosive climax of their love, sharing each other's breaths and basking in the brilliance of the sun that shone from the limitless blue of their particular and precious heaven.

In the night, she whispered, her mouth sweetly moist with his tasting, her lips bruised and burning from his insatiable invasion, 'I'll give you my support, darling, in whatever work you do. I'll earn for both of us, I'll keep the real world away from you so that you can live in your own world and create your masterpieces.'

'An artist,' he teased, pushing a leg between hers and following with his lips the now familiar paths all over her pulsating body, 'whatever his line, can't retreat to an attic studio and lose contact with worldly things. Everyday living, other people's sadness and joy—it's where a true creator of artistry or whatever draws his inspiration from. But I love you for the thought. Jemma,' he groaned, 'never change. Keep that expression in your eyes, that hungry love in your loins—look at you now,' he held away, smilingly looking her over, 'your entire body from head to curling toes—it's saying "I want more."'

She blushed, then reached out, but he deliberately held her from him, and she saw his glistening shoulders, felt on his chest the moisture of long, hard loving, inhaled the scent of desire on his skin.

He buried his face in her breasts and drew in her perfume, then, as if he would never be able to have enough of her, started the lovemaking all over again.

CHAPTER SIX

DRIVING away from work, Jemma's spirits soared. She was going home to Arne! He emerged as she entered, staring at her almost as if it had been her fault that the day had seemed so long.

Radiant, Jemma ran to him and was enfolded by the steel hawsers that were his arms. Hungrily, she reached up for his kisses.

When he swung her high and strode swiftly up the stairs, she hooked her arm around his neck, while with her free hand she began unfastening his shirt buttons. In the bedroom, he shed his clothes and they were flesh against flesh. He possessed her mouth, linking with her quickly as if his body had hungered all day for hers.

Jemma soared with him, her breath coming in gasps, her hands all over his hair, his face, his arms, while he savoured every secret part of her until that moment when her body moved in breathless spasms of ecstasy and total oneness with his.

A long time later, they were still entwined. So close were they, she could feel his chest's movements as though they were her own.

'I never thought,' he muttered against her throat, 'that a day could seem so endless. What is this thing I agreed to—that you, my wife, my woman, should go off every day to your *work*?'

Reprovingly, she shook his arm. 'Stop being a chauvinistic macho male, darling.'

'If I were,' he countered swiftly, 'would I have gone ahead and married you under those conditions?' He had spoken with an edge that pulled her up sharply, making her decide to be more cautious even when teasing him.

He had his pride, she must never forget that. He had given up a secure way of life to carve out a path for himself into the unknown, taking a chance on his future success in the world of art. And he had done so with her complete agreement.

'Of all things, darling,' she nuzzled up to him, 'you aren't that. I said it as a joke, that's all. Will you forgive me?' Her melting eyes sought his and he caught his breath, the lovemaking beginning all over again.

Later, the evening meal behind them, Arne said, 'We've been invited to a party. Next Saturday at the Forrests'. Any objections to going?' She shook her head. 'Even if you had,' he went on, 'I'd have overridden them. I want to show you off.'

'Like a piece of sculpture you've created?' she teased.

He laughed. 'Genius I am not,' he declared. 'It would have taken one to create you.'

Johanna's words came back to her. 'Arne's a near-genius, did you know that? Of course you didn't.' Now why, Jemma wondered, did the mere thought of the woman cause her stomach muscles to contract? She laughed to dispel her own tension.

'Well, *I* think you're a genius,' she remarked lightly, moving to seat herself on her husband's knee.

He rubbed his face against her hair, inhaling its scent. '"Gifted" is probably nearer the mark.' Then he groaned. 'Come love me again, sweet Jemma. I can't get enough of you into me.'

Laughing, head back under the trail of his kisses around her throat, she protested, 'But I've brought a load of work home with me.'

His change of mood was swift and frightening. Was it a sign of that underlying resentment she had dreaded and he had denied he would ever feel? He put her from him edgily. 'My God, I didn't realise how the roles would be reversed so drastically.'

Jemma was dismayed by his attitude. 'You agreed that I'd follow my career. At least for a year or two.'

'I must have been mad,' he muttered, then he saw her frown and her disconcertment. His arms went round her and he kissed her uncertainty away.

Smiling up at him winningly, she said, 'You promised to show me your studio, the place where you practise your painting and your sculpture——'

'And practice makes perfect?' He tipped her chin and kissed her eyes. 'I must remember that when I struggle with my shapes and figures and try to get the material in my hands to match up with the picture in my head.'

'It will come, Arne. One day you'll succeed. You might even make a sale, then you'd really be on your way, wouldn't you?' She pressed the tip of his nose. 'Then you wouldn't be officially classed as "unemployed" any more.'

He released her, smiling broadly. 'Forgive me, Jemma,' he pressed kisses across her mouth, 'but you do it so well. You look so irresistible when you straighten your lovely face and put on your "caring" tone, I want to——' He went to scoop her up but she twisted away.

'Lead me to it, Mr Drummond.' She tugged his arm. 'I can't wait to see your secret hideaway.'

It was an ancient barn, stone-built, once stacked with hay and farming implements, but renovated now and converted with a very different use in mind. Heating had been installed, and picture windows built in to give sufficient light.

Trestle tables were spread with cartridge paper covered in bold sketches of the human body, both male and female, intricate pencil prints of wild life and mother-and-child portraits. Against the walls, half completed paintings leaned, as if waiting for fresh artistic inspiration to add the finishing touches.

Bending down, Jemma read the signature on a still life. 'This isn't yours, is it?' she asked. 'It's by someone called Armin Power.'

'It's the name I use,' he answered, watching her.

'Is it?' She spoke the name. 'Sounds good. Sounds great. With a name like that, you can't help but succeed.' Her eyes softened. 'Arne, I may be completely ignorant of the basics of art, but even I can tell you're already a few rungs up the ladder. This really is something.' She indicated the painting she had inspected.

'Giving me the full treatment, aren't you. Like any beginner, your trained reasoning probably goes, I need my confidence boosted, plus a sackload of encouragement.'

'Why are you being sarcastic?' she asked, frowning. 'I hadn't suddenly turned counsellor. I meant every word. You're good, Arne. All this,' her hand swept round, 'shows——' in his prickly mood, dared she say it? '—shows great promise.'

'Thanks,' he answered briefly and moved to the door, inviting her to follow. In the house again, he remarked drily, 'Well, what's your considered opinion? Have you backed a winner in marrying me?'

Going to him, she pressed her body against his, resting her arms around his waist, her cheek against his chest, wanting to feel his warmth wrap around her, his arms holding her, his mouth taking over hers.

'Mr Drummond, sir,' she whispered, 'I'm putting all my money on you. I may not possess much in the way of artistic appreciation, but my intuition's telling me forcibly that the man in my arms is really going places. One day, darling,' her voice cracked, 'you'll be great. I'm certain of it.'

He responded with a fierceness of demand that told her how much he appreciated her loyalty and belief in him. Desire had its way and he swept her into his arms and up the stairs. Roughly he removed her clothes and as the fever of wanting coursed through her bloodstream, she peeled off his covering too. It was almost as if the end of the world—their world—was on its way and they might be parted for ever.

He gentled as their bodies made contact, easing her down, caressing her every curve and line with tongue and trailing hand until she arched towards him, crying, 'Oh darling, come to me now!'

Every evening it was the same. Her work forgotten, they would fall into each other's arms and make fiery, passionate love. Did Arne feel as she did, Jemma wondered one evening, lying fulfilled and content in his arms.

Did he sense as she sometimes did, although without any rational basis, that if they stayed too long apart, losing intimate contact, a volcano might erupt between them, throwing them each in different directions, never to find each other again?

For the Forrests' party, Jemma chose a glittering silver dress. Arne's eyes widened as he traced the outline of her slender body beneath the wrap-around style, its neckline high, yet hiding nothing of her attractions.

He walked towards her, hands in the pockets of his dark evening suit, his glance narrowed and intent.

'Jemma, my love,' he said softly, 'you're putting ideas into my head—like not going to the party and taking you to bed right now.' He reached out but she twisted away, laughing-eyed.

'It's taken me hours to dress like this. I bought this outfit in a mad moment, although I never thought I'd get around to wearing it. But——' With our beautiful hostess, she'd been intending to add, having once been your fiancée, I had to rise to the occasion and present my one-time rival with some competition.

Entering the Forrests' residence, Jemma saw that, in ambience and impact, the place was far more elaborate and showy than Arne's and her house would ever be. My tastes in furnishings and decorations, she reflected, are so different. With a shock she found herself wondering: Would Arne like the house we share to look like this? After all, if he'd married Johanna, this would have been his life-style, wouldn't it?

Dave greeted them first, hand extended. He eyed them cordially, but with his usual lack of animation. Johanna, glass in hand, was the sparkling centre of a circle. Arne, towering as he did above the other men in the room, was caught in her side glance. Her eyes swung round. She glided towards them, her green eyes sliding over Jemma's silver dress, then slipping back to Arne, holding his gaze.

Her body was swathed, from plunging neckline to neat ankles, in dazzling scarlet, its brilliance a perfect foil for her pale looks and blonde hair. Diamond earrings swayed in unison with her hips, a diamond necklace sending out sparkling messages from the white throat it adorned.

Why did I think, Jemma wondered bleakly, that even in this dress I'm wearing I could ever compete with this woman? Johanna's hand took Arne's and she led him across to the group she had left.

Jemma followed slowly, but Arne looked behind and took her arm. She went with him gladly, knowing it had been their hostess's intention to tear them apart.

He was greeted by the stretched-out hands of his former colleagues, who welcomed him as if they had not seen him for a year. They greeted Jemma too, but they saw her every day of their working lives. It was Arne they fastened on, absorbing him back into their world, taking him from her.

Cindy was there, hand in hand with her fiancé. Dragging him across to Jemma, she lifted a glass from a tray and wrapped Jemma's hand around it.

'You look just great,' Cindy exclaimed. 'Doesn't she, Bobby? Jemma, dear,' she whispered, 'our friend Johanna's *green* about the way you've outdone her. But watch it,' she added, eyeing their hostess, 'she's got her nose to the ground where your husband's concerned. See, she's hanging on to his arm just as if she's *his* wife and not our Dave's.'

Arne turned, meeting Jemma's eyes. Had he been seeking her out? She shivered with the shock of the electricity that passed between them. At the moment she moved to join him, he responded to Johanna's tug on his arm, laughing at something she said.

Trays of food were being carried round and Cindy seized a plate, handing it to Jemma. 'Grab some sustenance,' Cindy advised, helping Bobby and herself to some canapés. 'You'll need it to boost your energies for the fight.'

'What fight?' Jemma asked, following Cindy's example and chewing appreciatively.

'The one that's coming your way. Look at our Dave's wife feeding your husband with tasty mouthfuls. I hope he bites her fingers. If I were in your shoes, I'd go over and——'

'So who's supposed to be advising who?' asked Bobby, patting her arm. 'I thought that was Jemma's job.'

'That's OK, Bobby,' Jemma laughed. 'You'd be surprised how often counsellors need counselling. We're only human, after all.'

Dave Forrest broke away from his wife and beat a slow, straight path to Jemma's side. Out of the corner of her eye, Cindy picked up Dave's steady approach.

'You're going to have company,' she observed under her breath and tugged at her fiancé's hand, pulling him into the crowd.

'How's married life?' Dave asked with his watered-down smile.

'Just fine,' Jemma answered, drinking some wine and seeking her husband's tall figure.

Dave's eyes followed hers, fastening on to his wife's face as she glowed up at the man beside her. Not by the flicker of an eyelid did Dave display the slightest hint of emotion. Why, Jemma wondered, doesn't he gnash his teeth at his wife's blatant flaunting of her feelings for another man?

Since Dave showed no apparent inclination to converse, Jemma dispensed with her half finished drink, remarking, 'Arne showed me his studio. I think he shows great promise.'

By his nod, Dave appeared to agree. 'Has he told you——?'

TEMPTATION 🌹 YES PLEASE!

… send me my 4 FREE Temptations together with my FREE GIFTS. Please also reserve a special Reader Service Subscription for me. If I decide to subscribe, I shall receive 4 superb new titles every month for just £5 post and packing free. If I decide not to subscribe, I shall write to you within 10 days. The free books and gifts will be mine to keep in any case. I understand that I am under no obligation whatsoever - I can cancel or suspend my subscription at any time simply by writing to you. I am over 18 years of age.

8A8T

Yours Free! when you return this card.

(BLOCK CAPITALS PLEASE)

Name _____

Address _____

_____

_____

_____ Postcode _____

Reader Service
FREEPOST
P.O. Box 236
Croydon
Surrey CR9 9EL

NO
STAMP
NEEDED

SEND NO MONEY NOW

'That professionally he calls himself Armin Power? Yes, he has. I think it's great as a pseudonym.'

Dave seemed about to speak, but changed his mind.

Jemma became aware that Arne's attention was on them. Johanna, laughing, looked round, too. So close was she standing to Arne, she must have felt his move to break away. Then someone spoke to him, so it was Johanna who approached, eyes flashing and hard.

'Enjoying a cosy chat, you two?' Her gaze bounced between Jemma and Dave. 'Arne's annoyed, Mrs Drummond, that you've deserted him this evening.' She shot a glance at her husband, then smiled tautly at Jemma. 'Don't allow Arne too long a leash, Mrs Drummond. He just might give a mighty tug and land up in another woman's arms.' Her own arms stretched wide, and her eyes slewed tauntingly to her husband.

Dave made a sharp movement, but it was apparently just to place his glass on the table. Doesn't he have any pride? Jemma wondered. Why doesn't he react like any normal husband at such stark provocation?

I'll hit back for both of us, she resolved, gritting her teeth. She's not going to get the better of me! 'The love Arne and I share, Mrs Forrest,' Jemma countered with a studied calmness, 'is the kind that doesn't require either of us to cling to each other. But the moment we do touch, it bursts into spontaneous flame between us.'

Johanna's face paled and her indrawn breath was a hiss. 'Ask your husband who joined him on his *business* trip abroad,' she spat. 'Ask him that question, will you?'

'Maybe I will,' Jemma replied coolly, even though her heartbeats tripped and tumbled. Had Johanna won, after all?

'That's Arne's business entirely,' Dave snapped.

Johanna laughed in his face, eyes flashing. 'Is it?' she gloated. Turning to go, she collided with Arne's towering figure. Instead of moving to pass him, she pressed against his body, throwing back her head and gazing up at him.

Jemma, close to Dave, sensed his distress, felt a spasm shake him. His face was drawn, his shadowed eyes burned like dying embers fanned by a rogue wind.

Johanna walked away, throwing a provocative glance over her shoulder at Arne, while her hips and the diamond-drop earrings vied with each other again as they swung.

Arne, expressionless, watched Johanna go, then joined his wife.

'Sorry about that,' Dave muttered to Arne, the words slurring as if the turmoil in his mind were clouding his brain.

'That's OK.'

'Arne, darling,' Jemma slipped her hand through his arm and spoke with a false casualness, 'so who was the mysterious woman in your life who joined you while you were abroad? Dave's wife said——'

'We're leaving, Dave,' Arne said crisply. 'Thanks for the party.'

On the homeward journey, Jemma tried in vain to start a conversation. Questions begged to be asked, but she could not cross-examine this tight-lipped stranger.

Making for the drinks salver in the living-room, Arne clinked bottles. 'Jemma?'

'No, thanks.' That stranger was there in the room. When was the man she loved going to return? 'Arne,' she attempted to inject a note of detached interest into her voice, 'I'm taking a wild guess, but...was that mystery woman who joined you abroad—Johanna?'

'Got it in one,' he answered brittly. 'Johanna it was.' He tipped back his head, swallowed and went for another.

Jemma watched, a chill stealing over her heated skin.

'Let's start at the beginning, shall we?' Arne said, crossing to stand in front of her. 'In that year or so abroad, first and foremost, I travelled as Prospect Industrial's representative. But I also spent time on my own affairs, visiting galleries, attending exhibitions of my work.'

Jemma frowned. 'You've advanced *that* far in your studies?'

He dropped to the sofa, leaning back and crossing his legs and tapping the cushioned seat beside him. Slowly Jemma advanced, occupying the space. He took her hand but she was too taut to respond to the pressure of his fingers.

'All the same, I have a hell of a way to go. My work still has only an amateur status, Jemma, but I'm not a complete beginner.'

Silently, Jemma cursed her own ignorance of his subject. Even a tiny amount of artistic perception would have told her, on looking at his 'efforts' as she regarded them, that they were more than the 'gifted' he modestly admitted they might be.

'So—so where does Johanna come into this, Arne?'

'Johanna's a trained model. She's not just a businessman's wife.'

'A—a fashion model, you mean?'

'An artist's model,' he corrected.

Jemma recalled the sculpted figures she had seen around the house, some without recognisable features, others whose faces she thought vaguely that she had seen somewhere...

'Yours?' she whispered. 'Your model?'

He nodded. 'She's posed for me many times. She's also an excellent saleswoman, not to mention organiser of exhibitions. Plus, she has connections through her father.'

'She sold your work? Organised your exhibitions?' Arne nodded and Jemma wondered if her heart could sink any lower. Did Johanna possess not only almost perfect beauty but brains, too?

'Johanna joined me at intervals throughout the trip. It was a business partnership, pure and simple. I paid her a small fortune to go with me and work on my behalf.' He smiled wryly. 'Professionally, she doesn't come cheap. Dave agreed to the arrangement, provided his wife was not absent for too long at a time.' He took her hands. 'Adultery was not committed, Jemma. Believe me, whatever was between us ended long ago.'

For you, maybe, Jemma thought, closing her eyes and pulling away, but not for her. She's as crazy about you as she ever was, I'm certain of that. And as even Cindy saw, she's determined to get you back.

'Does all this mean,' she asked, 'that you're not really the unknown I took you to be? That the heights are already within your grasp?'

'Hardly.' He eased back against the sofa and spread his arms along its upholstery. '"Heights" is much too strong a word. You surely understand that there's a big difference between *gaining recognition* in the art world, as I'm doing at present, and earning sizeable fees for my work?'

His hand strayed to her hair, lifting it and stroking the sensitive skin beneath.

'I realise that,' she acknowledged, her nerves leaping at his caressing touch.

'The money even now isn't flowing in. Life won't be as easy as it would have been if I'd stayed on in my job.'

'I accepted that,' Jemma replied, 'when you proposed to me. It didn't worry me that I'd have to be the money-earner, that financially, things might be a bit difficult...' She was hit by a thought that stunned her. 'But Johanna couldn't take it? Am I right? You'd proposed to her, telling her of your plans, and she turned you down because of them?'

'It was one of the reasons. She couldn't see herself as the wife of a man who had no particular standing in society, and who, moreover, was intending to renounce a top industrial position, not to mention a lucrative one.'

'So she married Dave Forrest, who didn't have any plans to step down the social scale?'

'Correct again.'

But one day, Jemma reasoned, Arne would succeed. He would become well known, maybe even famous. Johanna wouldn't rest, would she, until she had got Arne—and his fame and fortune—securely into her life, regardless of the unhappiness she might cause to others.

Arne took her into his arms, kissing her throat, her cheeks, her lips. 'Jemma, let me reassure you—Johanna as a woman doesn't exist for me now. That time has passed. It won't be repeated. Do you believe me?' His dark, intense gaze played over her face and she could not conceal from him the love she felt so deeply.

'I believe you,' she whispered, as his mouth came down, claiming hers.

But do I really? she wondered, remembering Johanna's flashing, provocative eyes as they had moved over Arne that evening. I wish I *could* believe you, I only wish I could...

CHAPTER SEVEN

ONE evening, Arne paced the room, then, as if his own restlessness angered him, he swung Jemma into his arms. Lingeringly, then with a kind of rough impatience, he kissed her. With a feeling of dread, she sensed that there was something on his mind.

Whenever possible, they had made the most passionate love. Yet, even as their intimacy had deepened and their knowledge of each other's needs had increased, Jemma had become increasingly aware that, in some indefinable way, Arne was straying from her. It made her afraid and it would not let her rest.

If only she could discover a way into his world, she thought, a window through which she could gaze and try to understand the way his creative mind worked.

But, rooted as she was in the real world, the things that moved her to the brink of tears were not so much beautiful works of art as people coming to her with their troubles, problems which brought them almost to the edge of despair, but which she, with her training and knowledge, could do her best to help them solve.

For days now, she had sensed with a growing anxiety Arne's restlessness, his broad shoulders pushed straight as, with increasing frequency, he stared like a caged animal through the window.

Was he now going to say, 'That child we're intending to have one day—I don't want to wait any longer'?

It's still too soon, she thought agitatedly, gazing up into the sea-depths of his eyes; I love my job, but loving *him* so much, how can I refuse?

What he actually said—with a kind of anger—almost floored her.

'Jemma, I've got to get away.' His arms curled around her armpits and shoulders, hooking her to him. 'I need to find myself,' he went on. 'Do you understand?' He shook her slightly. 'I've got an exhibition coming soon. I've done work for it, but I need to do more.'

Jemma nodded, not knowing what else to do.

'I need to look on different things, explore possibilities that aren't obvious to me here. You must understand that this happens sometimes. There's a cottage on the Dorset coast I own. Come with me.'

Her heart lurched. This was his private, secret side which he hid from the world, and he was inviting her into it. *But she could not accept his invitation.*

'Go with you? Darling, it's impossible. My work——'

He almost threw her from him. Walking away, shoulders hunched, his eyes lashed the lawn, the paved terrace, the rose garden as if their very familiarity were to blame for his stale state of mind.

'To hell with your work,' he grated. 'I should have known you'd put that first. Right from the start you warned me, didn't you.'

There was a swell of almost physical pain inside her. To her trained mind, his bitter tone told of resentment stored up, being brooded over in private moments to be released at times of quarrel and clashes of temperament.

'Yes, I did,' she answered, her heart throbbing at the injustice of his attitude. 'You agreed I should keep my job.'

'So,' he swung round, 'take a break, a couple of weeks off.'

'Arne, I can't! My diary's booked solid, I've so many people to see, so many problems to find answers to.'

'Involved in everybody's life but mine.'

Shaking, her hand found her cheek. She sat down as if nursing an ache. Thoughts she never even realised her mind had harboured turned themselves into poisoned words.

'My world and yours,' she exclaimed, 'how can they ever meet? I'm in touch with reality, with everyday worries and problems. You stay here living in your own tight sphere, a world you've created—for yourself. You—you don't even know the meaning of the words hardship, poverty, misery.'

He hauled her up, gripping her arms. 'Oh yes, I know about such things, and they concern me, believe me. How else do I make my sculptures real, instead of just bits of insipid decoration? How else can I sincerely depict the human situation? Naked, unpalatable truths work at me, through me and into my work. So don't throw such accusations at me, Jemma.'

So she had misjudged him, she admitted miserably, rubbing her arms after he had released her. From her depths a sigh shook her.

'Arne,' she rested her palms on his chest, 'go to your cottage. Rediscover yourself, find your new ideas. But darling,' her eyes lifted sadly to his because the thought of being parted from him even for just a few days filled her with anguish, 'I can't go with you. Those appointments in my diary are people in trouble, coming to see me because they need my help. Some of them are desperate.'

He held her away, eyes slanting down at her upturned face. 'Suppose I said *I* was desperate—for you to come with me?'

She could only shake her head and rest her forehead against his chest, swallowing back the tears that threatened. 'Don't—don't lynch me,' she pleaded. 'You're pulling me in so many different directions I'm screaming inside.'

He forced her head up and stared into her depths, his lips moving on secret words and endearments. 'I'll make such love to you you'll have to come with me. Otherwise you'll feel you've lost a limb, that your heart's been removed, that your soul's gone missing——'

'Don't!' she cried. 'You're lynching me again.' A great sigh shook her body and she reached up, bringing down his face and covering his mouth with hers. 'Make love to me instead, darling, enough to last me the few days you'll be away.'

That night they burned with passion, flesh searing flesh, his mouth on her body making her give and give again, his hands tracing the paths of her greatest excitement, her knowledge of his needs making him groan and shudder and dominate and demand. Sometimes he was cruel, at other times gentle, and she never knew what his reaction would be to her ardent provocation.

Daylight crept into the bedroom's corners before they rested, fulfilled and filled with each other, bodies reluctantly relinquishing intimacy, hearts slowing down to a sleeping rhythm, lips touching now and then, even as they dreamed.

Cindy smiled as Jemma came into the office. 'You still look bridal,' she commented, grinning, 'even though it's a couple of months now, isn't it?'

Jemma nodded, picking up a pen, turning it end to end, remembering Arne's departure. He had stared down at his wife's naked body, put out a hand then pulled it back. 'If I touch you again, I'll never go,' he'd said, 'but my God, you're a magnet. If I look at you much more, I'll change my mind——'

'You must go,' she told him, springing up and pulling on a gown, 'otherwise you'll blame me for keeping you and——' Firmly, she tied the belt of her robe. It was like closing the door on their lovemaking. 'I'll see you off.'

He had kissed her lingeringly. 'I'm telling myself,' Jemma had said, 'that it's just like seeing my husband off on a business trip. It's part of your work, after all, darling, isn't it? Filling your eyes with fresh sights, breathing in different scents——'

'Listening to the sea, hearing the gulls cry, walking on the shore against the wind.' He had watched her narrowly for the effect on her of his images. Seeing the quick longing, he had followed up his advantage with, 'Now will you come?'

She had closed her eyes and shaken her head, not bearing to witness his disappointment, keeping her sorrow in. But it was with a touch of anger in his stride that he went to his car, throwing in his backpack with the few belongings he was taking.

Everything he needed for his work, he had explained earlier, was already at the cottage. Everything, he had added, except the one thing he really needed to activate his inspiration. His wife...

With a perfunctory salute in reply to her prolonged wave, he had driven from the house, profile set, attention switched to events ahead. If he had glanced back just once, he would have seen the handkerchief mopping Jemma's tears.

From ardent lover, he had turned into angry husband. But how could I have gone with him, she asked herself, her emotions in torment, glancing through her close-packed appointments schedule for the next week or so. I couldn't let all these people down.

Towards the end of the afternoon, Dave Forrest appeared in her office doorway. Putting aside her dismal thoughts about the lonely evening that stretched ahead, Jemma smiled her counsellor's smile and continued tidying her desk. Just what, she wondered, was the managing director of Prospect Industrial doing knocking on her door?

Her welcome shone through, despite the fact that seeing the man reminded her of a woman she would rather forget. 'Not an official visit, Dave?' she queried brightly.

'I leave you to be the judge of that.' He dropped into a chair, and looked at her with interest. 'Marriage to Arne suits you. He has a way with women, no doubt about that.'

Jemma forgave him for the tinge of bitterness. Arne was proving a magnificent lover and she could forgive any man for feeling envious.

'Yes, I'm happy,' she responded, 'exceptionally so.'

'Long may it continue.' The hint of rancour was there again. He rose and walked about. 'I suppose you know by now,' he stared though the window as if the moving figures outside were of enormous significance, 'that my wife models for Arne?'

Jemma picked up a paper clip and played with it. 'Arne told me that she used to, but——'

'She still does.' He turned as the sound of Jemma's sharp movement reached him.

She threw away the twisted paper clip. 'He said that Johanna had played a part in his life, but that it was over.' Her lips moved stiffly. 'I took it to mean they'd parted company completely.'

'On a personal basis, but professionally, no.'

'I see. I obviously misunderstood him.' Jemma did her best to sound reasonable and balanced about it all, desperately hiding the anxiety which was taking hold. 'Arne told me also that Johanna accompanied him for some of the time on his recent trip abroad.'

Dave nodded, taking the seat her clients usually occupied. 'She acted as his personal assistant wherever he exhibited. Her father owns a number of art galleries across Europe and he gave Arne space for his work. She took a lot of the hassle off his shoulders, like finding buyers and negotiating prices.' He made a pointed arch with his fingertips. 'She has a good brain, however much she may try to fool people by playing dumb.'

Jemma stared at her desk-top. That much she had begun to guess about this man's wife. What she had not realised was the extent of Arne's continuing involvement with his ex-lady-friend. He had not told her and it hurt. What had he said? *'Johanna as a woman doesn't exist for me now. Will you believe me?'*

She had tried, but now she knew how right she had been to doubt her ability to do so. It wasn't simply that, as Dave had just said, Arne 'had a way with women.' Johanna had a way with men, and one in particular— Arne Drummond.

'He's gone away,' she said dully. She glanced at her watch and forced a laugh. 'Only a few hours and I'm already missing him badly.'

Dave's smile was sympathetic. 'Since I've known him, and that's a good few years now, through his father and mine, he's needed these periods of solitude.'

'Artistic temperament?'

'Right. He has this cottage. It's his secret place. Never takes anyone there.'

Yet he invited me to go with him! Jemma thought. It was a wonderful compliment he was paying me... *and I turned it down.*

'Talking of one's own company,' Dave rose, 'I came to ask you——' He glanced outside. Employees of Prospect Industrial were making their way home. 'Look, it's time we both quit for the night. Like a drink somewhere?'

About to refuse, Jemma thought, Why not? There's no one at home waiting for me. 'Thanks, I'd like that. Your wife——?'

He shrugged his narrow shoulders. 'Away somewhere on her own business. She did tell me, but I've forgotten. Her father relies on her a lot. She's expensive—yes, even to her father—but she gives good value. Also,' he paused thoughtfully, 'she loves the social life attached to the public relations job she does for him.'

Cindy had left for home earlier and Jemma locked the office. People greeted them, some with distinct curiosity, as they made their way outside to the car park. There was a pub just out of town on the edge of the country.

Other employees of Prospect were at the bar and the same interested looks came Jemma's way. For heaven's sake, she thought, I am the company's counsellor, so why are their expressions saying, hey, folks, what have we here?

Did Dave Forrest have a problem? The idea took her by surprise.

They shared a bench seat. 'I wanted to ask you,' said Dave, leaning back, 'about accommodation.'

She looked at him sharply, then composed herself, hiding her frown.

'Before you married, did you share a flat or a house, or——'

'No sharing, Dave. I had a small flat, modern block, good area of London. Main bedroom overhead, a smaller one tucked away, sofa-bed in the living-area where extra friends could sleep if they stayed unexpectedly overnight. My parents gave me a loan to help me buy it. In fact,' she watched his hand playing with a coaster, 'I've been trying to decide whether to sell the place or rent it out.'

'Could I put my name forward as a prospective tenant?' His hand was a fist now, resting on the polished table-top.

'*You*, Dave?' He wanted a place of his own? And so badly, he was in a visible state of tension, his knuckles almost white? The niggle of worry she had felt earlier grew stronger. Where did Johanna figure in this?

'I guess I owe you an explanation.' He spoke jerkily. 'I just want a kind of hideaway. Like Arne.' His smile was faint. 'For a different reason, of course. My wife loves parties. She gives them endlessly. I'm not exactly the party type. I only socialise when my job makes it inevitable.' His smile seemed to stretch painfully now. 'Her parties go on for hours. I like my sleep. Not to mention my privacy. I can't call my place my own. Hence,' his palm turned upwards and Jemma saw its moistness, 'my request to you. Now do you understand?'

Oh, I understand, Jemma thought, more than a little relieved, realising now that her worries about the stability of his marriage were unnecessary. His reason for wanting a sanctuary was reasonable and acceptable. If he could afford to pay for such a bolt-hole in addition to the upkeep of his main residence, then why shouldn't he have one?

'I do, Dave. And yes, I'd be delighted to have you as a tenant.'

'There's another reason. I want my daughter with me.'

The world spun, swung round sickeningly, then righted itself.

'D-daughter?' Jemma stammered. Whose? she wanted to ask. Yours by a previous marriage? It surely couldn't be anything else. Could it?

'My wife and I have a child. Didn't you know?'

'You—you mean you adopted one?'

Dave looked at her curiously. 'No.'

Johanna had agreed to have Dave's baby, having refused to have Arne's? *Yet Arne would have married her if she had agreed?*

'Johanna sprang it on me, made the decision without telling me. No precautions. Marriage, then immediately, motherhood, here I come. When the pregnancy was confirmed and she told me, I didn't mind, far from it.' He brushed someone else's crumbs from the table-top. 'She's a beauty, Jemma. Just like her mother.'

There was no missing the pride. 'What's her name, Dave?'

'Tracey. Johanna chose. I didn't mind.' He swallowed a mouthful, replaced the beer mug carefully on the coaster. 'She's the light of my life.' His voice softened. 'I just want to see more of her, that's all.'

'She's away somewhere?'

'With her grandmother. Maternal. Johanna's too busy to look after her. I've lacked the confidence to bring her up single-handed, which is what it would have added up to if we'd kept her with us.'

'A handful, I expect?'

'You're implying I won't be able to cope with a toddler? You're right. But I know someone. My mother-in-law's baby-minder lost her secretarial job recently. She'd be willing to come and act as nanny.'

'Live in? The flat's not that big, Dave.'

'They could have the larger room?' His raised brows asked, Is it large enough? Jemma nodded. 'Then I'd have the smaller.'

He must want the child badly, Jemma thought, to contemplate squeezing his personal needs and privacy into an area that was little more than a shoe-box. Was it this, and not the peace and quiet he claimed to be seeking, that was motivating him to alter his habitat and environment so drastically?

'It might be why you haven't heard of my daughter's existence,' Dave went on. 'She rarely comes home. If either Johanna or I want to see her, we drive down to her grandmother's and spend the day, or the weekend.' He pushed away his empty glass. 'She cries when we leave. It——' he took a breath '—it breaks my heart.'

So, Johanna thought, playing with the strap of her handbag, the deadpan act is just the outer covering. Dave Forrest has a living, breathing heart beneath that expressionless surface. I should have realised, she reproached herself, I should have dug deeper.

There seemed to be a release of tension all over his body. Jemma felt it as he relaxed beside her.

'When do you want the tenancy to start?' she asked.

'As soon as possible.'

'That'll suit me fine. It doesn't do a place any good to leave it standing empty too long. Did you have a time limit in mind for renting it?'

He lifted a shoulder and hesitated, as if trying to find an answer, so Jemma prompted, 'Three months? Six?'

'Indefinitely?' he asked at last. 'I don't suppose my wife's socialising habits will change in the foreseeable future. They're too deeply ingrained for that.'

'Those parties would prevent you taking your daughter into your home?'

He nodded. 'You've heard the noise level, haven't you? You won't be wanting the place for yourself again, will you?'

'Oh, no,' Jemma smiled, 'never. I can't see Arne squeezing his big self into such a small living-area, neither his physical shape nor his broad artistic vision.'

Reaching home later, Jemma thought, I've just got to speak to him. Hearing his voice will be better than nothing. She was reaching for the telephone when the call came. Swiftly she spoke, hungering to make contact, as if her existence depended on it. If it wasn't Arne after all... It was, and Jemma closed her eyes with relief and happiness.

'Darling,' she murmured, trying to quieten her tumbling heartbeats, 'I was just about to call you.' She gave a shaky laugh. 'How—how are you living there, Arne? Like a beachcomber or a survivor from a shipwreck?'

'You could be right.' There was a smile in his words. 'I walk along the shore looking for shapes, driftwood, objects washed up.' There was a small pause. 'I walk along looking for you.'

The unexpected tenderness, the softening of his tone brought tears to her eyes. 'Oh, Arne, darling——'

'Come to me, Jemma. For God's sake, tell the world—
and your work—to go to hell.'

He wanted her in his secret place where he never took
anyone else... It was a compliment so great, Jemma
could hardly take it in. *Yet it was impossible.*

'Forget it,' Arne grated into the long pause. 'Forget
I ever said it.'

'Arne, don't you understand?' What was the use of
explaining all over again? 'Arne, this evening,' she
changed the subject to safer ground, 'Dave Forrest took
me for a drink.'

This time the pause was of his making. 'And?'

'He asked me about my flat. You know I hadn't decided what to do about it? Well, he said he would like
to rent it from me.'

'Did he tell you why?'

'His wife's party-giving habits, he said. He wants
somewhere to go, he said, when the crowds descend.
And, Arne,' she moistened her lips which had become
curiously dry, 'he wants his little daughter with him.'

The slightest of pauses, then, 'Does he, now?' Was
there just a trace of sarcasm?

'Arne, I didn't know they had a child, Dave and
Johanna.'

'What are you implying? That it's something I didn't
tell you?'

Why, Jemma wondered, did he sound so angry? Why
did I raise the subject at all. It might all fall through,
anyway. When Dave tells his wife he's thinking of moving
out, she might promise to change her ways... Anyway,
all I really wanted to do was tell Arne how much I loved
him...

'As a matter of fact,' he went on in the same hard
tone, 'I thought you knew. Prospect Industrial's grape-

vine's as efficient as most firms'. I thought it would have reached your ears via that route. You know how it goes,' with satire, '"Johanna Forrest's a lousy mother, leaves her child to be brought up by a grandparent," and so on.'

The sarcasm had bite, enough to leave tooth marks. Was he actually *defending* his ex-lover?

Arne, she wanted to say, Johanna wouldn't have your child, would she, but she had Dave's without question, *without even warning him what she was doing.*

A long-suffering sigh fanned around Jemma's ear. 'So I'll tell you why that child was conceived. Out of spite. Revenge. Against me.'

'For—for refusing to give up your dream of breaking away and fulfilling yourself as an artist? For not keeping your high-powered job so that you could keep her in luxury for the rest of her life? Even though she begged you to? Then she'd marry you?'

'Nine out of ten.' There was a prolonged pause. There had been a twisted note in Arne's voice. It could only mean that his pain had scarcely diminished over the years. So did he really marry me, Jemma agonised, as Johanna had alleged—for purely practical reasons?

'So what's been arranged?'

'About renting my flat to Dave? I asked him how long he'd want it for. He said indefinitely. His wife's party-loving habits wouldn't change, he said. I feel sorry for him, really, being driven from his own house be-cause——'

'Don't you know the real reason?'

Slowly, heavily, her heart began to sink. 'For Dave wanting a hiding-place? Of course. It's his wife's love of——'

'Their marriage is breaking up. Didn't he tell you?'

CHAPTER EIGHT

MORNING came slowly out of a restless night. Jemma had tossed and turned, reaching out her arms for a warm, hard body, finding only emptiness. She had heard his voice in her dreams. 'Come here to me,' he had said over and over.

'I can't reach you,' she had cried, her fingers groping, trying to catch his hand that was extended, only to miss and fall down and down, hitting rock bottom and waking with a sob.

The marriage is breaking up... 'No, no, not ours,' she had shouted to the cold mask in her terrible dreams, 'it's Dave Forrest's you're talking about.'

But saying that didn't make the dream any better. Johanna, broken away from anchor, floating free of the man she had married... Johanna, arriving like a piece of beautiful, irresistible flotsam on Arne's particular piece of beach... a shape for him to model, a woman for him to mould like clay, to take in his arms... *to love in his wife's absence!*

The call didn't come that evening, so she dialled and listened. And listened in vain. He must be out, she thought; wandering along the edge of the sea again, or climbing cliffs. Or even having an evening meal some- where, returning for a while to civilisation, if only to make comparisons?

She knew she was inventing acceptable reasons for his absence, for his failure to answer her call. He might even be sitting there, she imagined painfully, watching the

116

telephone ring, knowing it's me, refusing to answer to hurt me, passing his pain on to me. Because I won't go to him, and deciding it was no use trying again to persuade me.

Her head went down on the table, on her folded arms. If she let herself go, she would be crying at the intolerable, insoluble situation that existed between them. With a ragged sigh, she braced herself for an evening of small talk, pleasantries, of showing Dave round the place that was once her home.

He was delighted, he said, with everything. 'OK, it's not large,' Dave admitted, 'but that's all the less to keep tidy and clean.' He turned to her with a slight smile. 'You're not charging me enough, you know. I'd willingly double it——'

'As far as I'm concerned,' Jemma returned, 'you can have it for free. I don't need the money. Arne and I— we're fine moneywise at the moment. We've got it all worked out.'

Dave took her for a meal. It was the least he could do, he said, he was so grateful to get such a pleasant roof over his head. 'When I've settled in myself, I'll collect my daughter and Moira.'

'While I remember,' she raked in her bag, producing keys, 'I'll hand these over. Your tenancy can begin tomorrow if you like.'

He pocketed them. 'I feel I should sign an agreement or something.'

Jemma smiled. 'I trust you, Dave. I know it's not being very businesslike, but——' she lifted her shoulders which, in the low-cut, sleeveless summer dress she wore, glowed smoothly in the subdued lighting.

Dave's eyes followed the line of them, lingering on the attractive swell beneath the closely-cut floral fabric.

'Arne's a lucky guy, Jemma.' He spoke as if his throat were tight.

'But Dave,' Jemma's colour rose at the appreciation in his regard, 'Johanna's beautiful.'

'Beauty she has in plenty, sure.' He pushed away his coffee-cup. 'Warmth, understanding,' he glanced up at her, then down, 'compassion in her look, no. What's beauty, compared with what you've got?' The words seemed to burst from him out of control.

Oh God, no, Jemma thought. Rejected by his wife—if that's what's happened—he mustn't turn to me...

He went back to her house, hers and Arne's, for coffee. Seated, he leaned back, saying little. Jemma was tired, her mind drifting to Arne on his seashore. Did he lie there at night listening to the waves breaking and thinking of her? As she spent her every waking moment, night and day, thinking of him? Or did he have another woman in his thoughts...

She pulled herself up sharply. If she was so worried about her husband's faithfulness, she reprimanded herself, why didn't she join him? Then she thought about those people who came, day after day, to her office, seeking her advice, her practical help, her sympathy.

Dave seemed content to stay where he was, but she wished he would open his eyes and see how weary she was. Other people's problems, added to her own, were a weight she sometimes felt it was hard to bear.

The phone rang and she made a dive, knowing instinctively that it was Arne. Quickly, she urged herself, before he rings off, thinking you're in bed.

'Where the hell,' he challenged, 'have you been all evening? I've lost count of how many times I've tried——'

'Showing Dave my place, darling,' she broke in. 'Then he treated me to a meal. He's—he's here, Arne. Having a late coffee.'

'So what else is on the menu?' It was almost a snarl. 'Coffee's hardly a sleep-inducer.'

'Arne! What are you implying? For heaven's sake——'

Dave was on his feet, at the door, lifting a hand in salute. He made a face, guessing Arne's reaction. 'Tell him I'm going,' he mouthed. 'See you.'

'He's—he's gone, Arne.' Her own anger surfaced. 'Is that how much you trust me? On what do you base your judgment of my morals—your own?'

There was a long silence and Jemma could have bitten her tongue. Had he gone?

'OK.' He spoke with infinite weariness. 'I apologise. It's the distance between us, Jemma. My empty arms are killing me. I——'

'If it's any comfort, darling,' she whispered, 'I'm aching for you, too.'

She could hear the air being sucked into his lungs, heavily. 'So when's Dave moving in?'

'To my place? Don't know for sure. Tomorrow, probably. Arne, I've been trying to work out how to get a few hours free to——'

'Join me? Well?'

'It's not going to be easy, darling, but——'

'Look, I know your job's difficult, Jemma. I don't want to make it even harder. Just tell Dave Forrest "hands off". And...remember me, will you?' The phone rattled to rest at his end, severing the link. She was left looking at the silent receiver in her hand.

* * *

Dave took possession of Jemma's flat next day, giving her rent for six months in advance. He would allow himself a week or two, he told her, to settle in before collecting his daughter.

Most evenings Jemma spoke to Arne. Sometimes, meetings or consultations would keep her out late. Or Arne would be working in his studio, out of reach of the telephone. Deliberately so, he had told her on one occasion, since any disturbance could throw him for the rest of the day. Or night, if he decided to indulge the urge to create in the dark hours.

Ideas were coming thick and fast, he said. The London exhibition of his work was moving nearer with every passing day.

'From tomorrow,' he said one evening, 'I'll be out of reach. Until further notice.'

'Arne, won't I even be able to speak to you?' She couldn't keep the dismay from her voice.

'Not until I ring you. There's this shadowy dream I keep having, I've got to capture it. You understand?'

'I'll try, darling. I'll try.' She only just managed to stop her voice from breaking.

A couple of weeks passed. Jemma lost count of the times her hand stretched out to the phone. Tonight, she promised herself, I'll call him... just a few rings, and if he answers, I'll say, 'Hi, darling, I love you. That's all. You can go now.'

It was Friday afternoon, and yet another weekend stretched ahead.

Jemma, staring through the window, jumped at the hesitant knock.

'Miss Hale?'

'Hi, Pam.' Jemma was her professional self, smiling at the girl in the doorway. 'My goodness, you look happy. Things going well for you these days?'

'Tomorrow, Miss Hale,' Pam confided eagerly, 'me and Shane, my boyfriend—we're getting married.'

Jemma rose, her eyes lighting up. She grasped Pam's hands. 'I hope—no, I *know* you'll be very happy. You've given it some thought——?'

'Living together isn't enough, we decided. It'll be a civil marriage, Miss Hale.' Pam hesitated, pushing at her hair. 'But there's one thing—one person—we need. Someone else to act as witness. My mum and dad——' she shook her head, a fleeting sadness in her eyes '—so do you think you could——?'

'Fill the gap? Nothing I'd like to do more, Pam. Tell me the time and the place, and I'll be there.'

Pam was radiant, her dress pale blue, her dark hair shining. Her fiancé was tall and fair and smiling. Brett, Shane's brother, taller and fairer, shared his bag of confetti with Jemma, and as the couple emerged into the sunlight, they were showered in flakes like tinted snow.

Standing with the best man, Jemma saw them off in Shane's ancient car. Pam had put her arms around her, kissing her cheek. When she pulled away, there were tears in her eyes. 'Thanks, Miss Hale,' she whispered, 'for making this day come good. You've been like family to me.' She had bitten her lip and turned away abruptly, getting into the car.

Waving madly as they had driven off, Pam's happiness was back, her face glowing.

Someone was in the house. As soon as she stepped inside, she sensed a presence. A zipped jacket hung on the coat stand, *Arne's jacket.*

Dropping everything, Jemma ran, halting in the living-room doorway, eyes brilliant, breath coming jerkily. He was at the window and she cried to his back, 'Arne, darling, darling. Am I dreaming? Oh, tell me I'm not. I——'

He turned slowly, his face a mask, eyes icy. With de-liberation, he peered past her. 'Well, where's Dave? He needn't run for cover. We'll be civilised about this.'

He couldn't mean it! 'How do I know, Arne? I haven't seen Dave since yesterday evening.'

He was bronzed and toughened from sea air and early morning runs along the shore. His shirtsleeves were rolled, the hair on his forearms bleached. His leisure trousers clung around the leanness of his hips, the belt a notch tighter, Jemma was certain, than when he had left.

'So where have you been?' His words dripped cyni-cism, his expression caustic. 'Solving people's problems? Out of hours? On a Saturday afternoon?'

'In a sense,' she retaliated, trying to still her shaking hands. 'You could call it that.'

He eyed her soft peach suit, white frill spilling over at the neck, matching white bag and sandals. 'All dressed up? He must have been some guy.'

'There was a man in it,' she conceded, knowing her answer would probably goad him still more. 'You could say,' she said carefully, 'I've been playing a part. *In loco parentis*, I think that's what they call it. Filling a void caused by missing parents.'

'Kids? Whose?'

She shook her head, her dark hair swinging, framing her face, her cheeks still flushed from excitement at his arrival and the alcohol she had not had the heart to refuse. 'Not kids.'

Removing her jacket, she placed it carefully on the back of a chair. His eyes watched her every movement, moving to her slender hips, upwards to the provocative curve of her breasts.

'Remember the girl you were kind enough to find a room for? At your brother's house? Pam Lee?' She waited for his recollection, his slow nod. 'She asked me to her wedding. It was this afternoon.'

'Enjoy the party?' There was a slight curl to his lips. Even now, she thought, bewildered, she had not been able to restore his belief in her.

'So what do I have to do,' she shot at him, 'swear on oath that I haven't been unfaithful?' His steady gaze did not flicker. 'There wasn't a party, Arne,' she added tiredly. 'Pam's fiancé had his brother in attendance, whereas she had no one, no parents, no family. They wouldn't come, she told me. They turned her out, remember.' She sank into a chair. 'So I took their place, mother and father both. When she thanked me, she nearly cried with gratitude.' Her eyes lifted, holding his. 'If that was work, then, yes, I spent this afternoon solving other people's problems.'

There was a faint curve to his mouth. 'You're so dedicated to your work, I can't believe it.' His voice held admiration, not criticism. He moved towards her, step by slow step, eyes glinting. 'So I need help. I've got this problem. I need a woman. So badly I can't sleep at nights.' His fingers slid beneath his belt. 'I can't create. I can't even think in a straight line, let alone curves and angles.'

He dragged her upright and into his arms. 'Trouble is,' his eyes pierced through to her very soul, 'no other woman will do. Only you, Jemma. Only you can give me the release I crave.'

His mouth lowered to trail her throat, her mouthline, her eyes. As he moved, she glimpsed the flash of pain in his eyes. He had the look of a man who had suffered. Her heart stood still, then pounded. He was aching for her as she had been aching for him!

When he kissed her, her hands wrapped around his head, her lips parted to his probing, as he drank from the very source of her love, drawing her into him.

Then he wanted more of her and with impatience, brushed the white frill of her blouse aside, unfastening the buttons while his mouth continued to plunder hers. His hands found her breasts and she shivered at the touch of them.

He carried her upstairs, her hair swinging over his arm. Standing her down, he lifted away her garments one by one, kissing each and every part of her heated flesh, drawing back at last and filling his eyes with her glowing nakedness. Then, like a man appeasing a deep, unbearable hunger, he bent and kissed the seductive swell of her breasts, curling his tongue around the piquant points until she moaned with pleasure.

He had shrugged free of his shirt, his broad shoulders muscled and strong, his bronzed torso drawing her eyes, her lips making little dives, placing soft, provoking kisses all over it. Her face nuzzled in the fine dark hair and she laughed up at him as it tickled her nose.

He laughed, too, and guided her hand to his belt, telling her to unbuckle it. He looked down at her indulgently, but her movements were too slow for him and he threw aside the rest of his clothing, gathering her to his thighs and legs, letting her know of his hard, thrusting need of her.

Then they were lying together and the sweet familiar scent of him, the hard, demanding touch of hands that

brought stone and bronze to life and made her body
writhe and twist; the devouring kisses that bruised her
mouth and made her lips throb along with her desire-
drugged body—all combined to lift her from the reality
to which she was so securely bound to the absolute limits
of sensation and delight.

He possessed her as if he couldn't get enough of her
around him and into him, then he took her with him to
the summit of sensation, until they rocked, interlocked
and indivisible, on the very pinnacle of shared, total
fulfilment.

Dawn broke and still he wanted her, and she gave and
gave, taking too, making her own demands, which delighted him. He seemed tireless and insatiable, brushing
fatigue aside, showing no signs of tiring of taking her,
growing more and more demanding.

Wherever he led she went, delighting in his knowledge
of women's needs, learning more and more about the
man she had married. Yet even at the end, when, satiated
beyond words, they lay in each other's arms, she had to
acknowledge that her husband remained a mystery, one
problem, she told herself bemusedly, she would never
be able to solve.

He had gone when the sounds of the morning, of
everyday living, grew more and more intrusive. Sleepily
she had reached out to him, wanting to keep him with
her, yet knowing he had to go.

His creativity, he had whispered against her mouth,
was reinvigorated, his hands were itching to turn his ideas
into tangible form. 'My heart, my woman, my fantastic,
beautiful lover. I'm the one,' he kissed her breasts,
savoured her lips, rested a possessive moulding hand on
her stomach, stroked her thighs, 'who's being lynched

now. Torn apart, tugged away from you by my work, yet crazy to stay.'

Her arms wrapped around him. 'Quits, darling? Admit it.'

'Quits.' A touch of flint entered his sea-deep eyes. 'But when all's said, isn't it a question of where one's loyalty lies?'

Unable to adjust quickly to his change of mood, she was slow to respond. By the time she had asked, 'Arne, what do you mean?' he had gone. She lay there for some time, aghast that, beneath all the passion and wonder of their lovemaking, his resentment against her decision to continue working, and worse, her refusal to go with him to his hideaway, still festered in his mind.

He did not call her that night as she had hoped, nor did he answer the phone when she rang. Days passed and she did not hear from him, until one evening, there was an answer to her call.

She waited for him to identify himself, but all he said was a sharp, 'Yes?'

'I—it's me, Jemma.' She was thrown off balance by his abruptness. Then with a strained smile, 'Remember?'

'Jemma.' One word, but full of strange relief. 'I've been working like someone inspired. I've hardly stopped. You understand?'

'I understand,' she answered huskily. 'I've got to, haven't I?'

He paused. 'You have. Just as I have to try to understand your attitude to your work when it keeps you away from me.'

He thought her comment was a criticism of his decision to live away from her in his cottage. I hadn't meant it that way, she thought—had I? Do I, deep down, she wondered, feel this terrible resentment, too? Do we two really belong together, with me being so practical, and Arne living on a higher plane altogether? I *told* you, she wanted to cry out to him, that I had no imagination. You're a near-genius, Johanna claimed, and knowing you as well as she does, she's probably right. I'm not even in your league... She covered her eyes, despairing. Would these problems that kept dividing them never end?

At the weekend, there was a call from Dave. 'Could you come?' he asked. His voice sounded strange. 'If you've got other plans, that's OK, but——' He sounded as if he needed a strong drink.

'Sure I'll come,' she reassured him and wasted no time. She knew, by now, a cry for help when it came.

He was seated at the table, slumped over it, empty glass in his hand. He had had that drink, and it had done him no good.

His heavy eyes lifted to Jemma's. 'She's got Tracey, Jemma. My wife's got my child. She refuses to tell me where she's taken her.'

Jemma sat cornerwise to him, covering his hand with hers. 'So what happened to bring this about?'

After a long pause, he answered, 'I went to my mother-in-law's last night, as I'd arranged. To pick up my daughter and the nanny.' He drew in a long breath. 'Johanna was there. She said her mother had told her I was coming and that since I'd as good as left her, I was probably intending to try to assume custody of our child. Johanna said over her dead body. She was taking her right now, she said, somewhere where I wouldn't find her. Then she went. She'd take me to court, she said. But God, Jemma, we're not divorced, not even separated yet. All I've done is move out for the sake of peace and quiet. It's only temporary. You know that.'

Jemma shifted her chair nearer to Dave's, putting her arm around his shoulders. He needed comfort and she was offering it. His head turned and rested against her breast. She cradled it there. He was weeping dry tears and she was touched to the heart.

There was more to it, she reflected sadly, than the absence of his child. Insight told her that Dave Forrest loved his wife very dearly and was crying for her, too.

'So this is how things stand between us, is it?' The silky, feminine voice twined itself around them, making Jemma shake with fright. Dave's head shot up.

Johanna dangled a key. 'You got a spare cut for me, darling, remember?' she taunted. 'That was a mistake, wasn't it. Whoever heard of a man fool enough to give his wife access to his secret lover's apartment?'

Jemma got to her feet. 'I'm not your husband's lover, Mrs Drummond,' she said quietly, 'and you know it.'

'But I don't, do I? I frighten you both out of your guilty wits, catching you red-handed making love——'

'Be quiet, Johanna,' Dave, white-faced, said through his teeth.

Seeing his face, the heavy eyes, the misery they held, Johanna was visibly shaken, but it took her only a few moments to recover. 'So what was sweet, *innocent* Mrs Drummond doing with her arm round you,' she drawled, 'her great counselling act? Listening to your problems——'

Goaded out of his characteristic reserve, Dave ground through his teeth, 'Where's my child?' His fist hammered the table. 'Tell me where she is, or I'll——'

'Oh, but you won't, darling,' Johanna returned with a secret smile, 'because you know there's nothing you can do. *Nothing*.' She swung on her heel, pausing at the door. She looked from Jemma to her husband. 'I've seen all I need to see. A judge will know which parent is best suited to have custody of *our child*.'

She slammed out of the room, her feet ringing on the stone steps of the apartment block.

Jemma stayed with Dave for the rest of the evening. 'Will you find her for me?' he pleaded. 'Discover where my wife's taken my daughter?'

Jemma was horrified at the request. It was not part of her job as Prospect's counsellor to undertake such a task, but she knew that if she refused, Dave could switch his plea to asking her the favour as a friend.

'I'm not a private detective, Dave,' she conceded at last, 'but I'll do my best. It might take some time. You do understand?'

He had nodded and reached out to grasp her hand again.

A week passed, filled with appointments and interviews. They had given her no time to follow up Dave's request; they had, in fact, almost pushed it to the back of her thoughts. Something else had happened, too, to occupy her mind, to keep her thinking in between problem-solving by day, and well into the lonely, dark hours.

She had begun to suspect that she was expecting Arne's baby! A few days later, a test proved positive and she almost cried with joy. For the whole of that wild and passionate night they had spent together, there had been no barriers between them. Jemma had thrown caution to the winds, not giving a single thought to the consequences.

Maybe she had deep down, she reflected, but maybe, too, she had been desperate to discover a solution to this separation from him that had made her so miserable, and had deliberately suppressed all thoughts of how the whole course of her life might—just might—be changed by their lovemaking.

When I tell him, she thought, when he hears that his waiting is over and the child he wants so much will before many months have passed, be born to him, he will be more than delighted. All our problems will be resolved and we'll be together again. I'll be giving him the one thing he wants most in the world—a child of his own.

Staring through the window, she fretted that none of her phone calls to him in the past few days had been answered. Dave had asked her how her enquiries about the whereabouts of his little daughter had been going, but she had had to answer frankly that the few calls she had made had drawn a blank. Nor had she had much time, she had had to tell him, to spend on the problem.

'If you could think of a plan yourself, Dave...'

He had responded tonelessly, 'I'm going to have to stir myself out of this terrible apathy, I suppose, and do some investigating. Is that what you're implying?'

''Fraid so, Dave. Just at the moment, I——'

No, she wouldn't tell him yet. Her husband must be the first to know...

Now she stirred restlessly. There had to be some way to talk to Arne. She glanced at the time. Then it came to her. I'm going to him, she thought, pushing aside in her mind the work she had brought home to fill the long, lonely weekend hours.

Early Sunday morning, the traffic was mostly local, with only short distances to cover. Whereas she was driving to a relatively distant destination and her whole future stretched stupendously before her. She was expecting a child, hers and Arne's. Now it had been confirmed, her heart soared at the thought. Why, she asked herself, hadn't she known just how much she had wanted a baby—Arne's baby? Why had she wasted so much time fooling herself that her career came first, before her husband, before her marriage, even before her own happiness and fulfilment?

Nearing the coast, she had to ask the way two or three times. At last she found the tiny village, a collection of stone-built houses. Parking the car, she walked through the main street which lost itself eventually on the sandy beach.

'Seascape Cottage?' a local inhabitant replied. 'Up there, miss, part way up the cliffs. There's a path of sorts leading up to it.'

She was so near now, to Arne and to the moment she had been waiting for ever since she had known for certain...

Half-way, she stopped, staring at the slate-roofed building, more of a small house than a cottage. The wind lifted her hair and roughened the sea. The sun shone, breaking free of the clouds.

Voices lifted on the strong breeze, a woman's raised in laughter, a child, tiny, fair, ran a little unsteadily, over the sands. A tall man shouted encouragement, holding out his arms, crouching down as she reached him.

He held her between his knees and, to her delighted laughter, nuzzled her cheek. Then he straightened, lifting her high above his head, lowering her and kissing her forehead. It was plain he loved her dearly.

The mother came to stand beside them, putting her arm round his waist and resting her head on his shoulder. They made a perfect family tableau, a loving couple with the fruits of their love in the father's secure, encircling arms.

Except that they were not a family; the woman was another man's wife, the child hers alone ... the man was not that child's father. Or was he?

The question screamed in Jemma's head. Swaying, sickened by the sudden certainty that Johanna had in fact borne Arne's child but, out of bitterness and revenge, had had that child under the cover of her marriage to Dave, Jemma turned and made her way blindly downwards, stumbling a little on the loose stones.

There was a shout and Jemma hesitated, but plunged determinedly on. 'Jemma!' It was Arne and there was incredulity in his voice. When she didn't stop, it came again, angrily this time. *'Jemma!'*

She halted at the foot of the path, her sandalled feet on sand now. There were footsteps—Johanna's feet, light and quick, Johanna's silvery tones addressing her.

'Discovered my secret at last, Mrs Drummond?'

Slowly, Jemma turned, keeping her gaze averted from Arne. 'You mean the place you've run to with your child to hide her from Dave? Yes, as you can see, I've discovered it.'

Arne was approaching, the child in his arms forcing him to pick his way with care.

'No, Mrs Drummond. I meant—*who the father of my baby really is.*'

Johanna watched Jemma's face drain, saw her slight sway with immense satisfaction. Now it was put into words, Jemma felt the truth of it hit her between the eyes. So this was why Arne had so carefully kept Tracey's existence from her. He knew the truth of her parentage, too. *But she was certain that Dave did not doubt that he was the child's father.*

Yet even now, it seemed, Arne was attempting to deny the part he had played in the little girl's birth. 'For God's sake, Johanna,' he said, 'you know what you're saying isn't true.'

'Oh, isn't it? An eight-months child, they called her. A euphemism, darling—in Tracey's case, anyway—for conception before marriage. You know how things were between us.'

'And you damned well know that——'

The little girl began to whimper and his attention was distracted. He tried to pacify her by pulling a small doll from his pocket, but the angry tones seemed to have frightened her.

Johanna spoke loudly over the child's cries. 'And there's something you don't know, Arne darling—that your wife is up to her neck in an affair—with my husband.'

Arne's head came up, his burning eyes branding Jemma through to her heart. 'Is this true?'

'You know it's not,' Jemma cried to Johanna. 'What you saw meant nothing.' How weak that sounded, she thought with dismay; they were the traditional words of a guilty wife trying to deny her complicity. 'Dave was worried to death about Tracey's disappearance, and I was comforting him.'

'*Comforting him*? With his head on your breast?' Johanna exclaimed in a 'beat that' tone. 'And your arms cradling him against you, *holding him there*?' She flashed a triumphant glance at Arne, then turned its hard brilliance on to Jemma. 'Is that how you treat *all* your male clients, Mrs Drummond? No wonder you wow them all as Prospect Industrial's counsellor. No wonder the men line up at your door, eager for their own private share of your comfort——'

Spontaneously, Jemma's hand lifted, but Arne's shot out, capturing it. He's actually *protecting* her, Jemma thought unbelievingly. His fingers were cruel and bruising, his fury encapsulated in that one hold on her body.

'Is this true?' he demanded.

Jemma winced at the extra pressure he imposed. 'That Dave's head was where Mrs Forrest said it was? Yes, it's true. But,' her eyes, in her anguish, appealed to him for understanding, 'what I said just now was also true. I was comforting him.'

Johanna's crude laugh rang out. Arne handed the child to her and took a threatening step towards his wife.

His lips drew back in a sneer. 'Why, you——'

Jemma stood her ground, her heart pounding. 'For heaven's sake, Arne, I was fully dressed.' She spoke wildly, but realised how feeble the excuse sounded. Johanna had taken the incident completely out of context and presented it in the most harmful light possible.

'Darling,' Jemma held back the tears which nudged the backs of her eyes, 'do you honestly believe I'm capable of having an affair with another woman's husband? Surely you know me better than that?'

Arne was unmoved by her plea. Tight-lipped and furious, he grated, 'I obviously don't know you at all. And from now on, I find I have no inclination whatsoever to get to know you any better.'

He swung round and made for his cottage.

'Arne!' Her cry rang out over the sound of the waves breaking on the shore, breaking, she thought, like my heart. 'There's no affair between Dave and me,' she cried, 'you just have to believe me.'

He did not turn, nor even pause.

I'm having your baby, she longed to tell him, but he just kept on climbing, striding away from her—and out of her life.

A smug smile spread across Johanna's face. With her child in her arms, she watched Jemma walk slowly away, her footsteps dragging heavily through the sand.

CHAPTER NINE

'DAVE? I've got some news. Could I see you this evening?'

'Must it wait until then?' he asked, anxiety sharpening his voice over the internal phone.

Jemma glanced at the open door between her office and her secretary's. 'I'm afraid it has to, Dave. It——' she compressed her lips, 'it concerns us both. Could I call in and see you?'

'You're welcome any time. It's your flat, after all. Let yourself in. I've got a late afternoon meeting. I might be delayed. We'll go somewhere and eat.'

'That's OK, Dave. I'll get us a meal.'

'Fine.' A brief pause. 'Jemma, I wish you'd tell me——'

'Later, Dave. It's best.'

Jemma stood at the bedroom window—her room and Arne's—and stared through her tears at the distant hills. The day before, in a few short moments, her life had collapsed about her feet. All she could do now was to pick her way through the rubble and attempt to rebuild her life. Just the way she had told so many of her clients to do in the past, never dreaming that, one day, she would have to take her own advice, swallow her own medicine and like it.

I can't stay here, she thought, in this house—Arne's. Her self-respect would not allow her to remain. Arne did not trust her. Hadn't he as good as said so yesterday? Hadn't he demonstrated that he thought so little

136

of her loyalty and love, he didn't even doubt Johanna's allegation that she was indulging in an extra-marital affair?

Or was his love for Johanna so strong that it made him deaf to his wife's denials? Had he seized on those accusations of hers as a way of justifying and excusing the resumption of his own affair with Johanna?

The lies he had told, Jemma thought, about himself and Johanna. Her throat thickened with tears as she remembered his words. 'What was between us ended long ago...Johanna as a woman doesn't exist for me now...' *But what about Johanna as his child's mother?*

That was one secret she had to keep from Dave, and nothing, she vowed, would drag it from her—the truth about Tracey's parentage. Dave adored the child—that much was certain. 'She's a beauty; she's the light of my life,' he had said. 'She cries when I leave and it breaks my heart.'

What a lucky little girl, Jemma thought, to have *two* fathers loving her... With a catch in her breath, she placed the palm of her hand on her still-flat stomach.

This baby would only have a mother to love it, but, she vowed, I'll give it all the love I possess. With my heart and soul, I'll devote my life to it. This baby is all I've got left now, she thought brokenly, of the man I love so much.

'So where is she, Jemma?' Dave demanded, bursting into the flat much later, throwing politeness to the winds in his eagerness to hear the news. 'Where's Tracey? Is she well?'

His return had been delayed, as he had warned. It was late and the meal had been waiting for some time.

'She's fine, Dave.' If Jemma's voice was flat, her manner dispirited, he did not seem to notice. 'She's with Johanna, as you probably guessed.'

'Yes, but *where*, for heaven's sake?'

They were in the tiny kitchen and Jemma continued to serve the meal. 'Yesterday,' she told him, 'I went to Arne's hideaway. I just—had this overpowering need to see him.' She couldn't tell Dave the real reason for that 'need'—that she was expecting Arne's child, any more than she could now tell Arne. 'They're there, Dave, Johanna and Tracey. I saw them on the sands, with Arne. I—I didn't get to see inside Arne's cottage.'

She paused, as if too involved in her work to go on. It was necessary to think quickly, to choose her words. 'Johanna admitted I'd discovered her secret.'

'You mean where she'd taken Tracey?'

Jemma nodded, glad that he accepted what was only the partial truth. 'Let's eat, then I'll tell you the rest. Agreed?' She smiled encouragingly and he took his seat at the table.

By the end of the meal, she had told him everything he needed to know, including Johanna's accusations about themselves. He sat back, scandalised. 'Where's that phone?' he said. 'I'll get on to Arne——'

'No, no, Dave,' Jemma hastened to tell him. The last thing she wanted was a stand-up row between the two men. 'Arne wouldn't listen. Johanna's poured her poisoned words about us into his ear, and——' it still hurt to remember the way Arne had accepted the other woman's statement without question, '—and he believed her. You see, I—I had to admit it was the truth, Dave. Didn't I? I mean, she saw us sitting here, me with my arms round you, and you with your head...'

'And,' his lips tightened, 'Johanna being the woman she is, she enlarged it out of all proportion? Infused it all with a more sinister meaning, twisting the situation round entirely for her own ends?'

Jemma nodded, pouring coffee and pushing a cup towards Dave. He looked as though he needed it. His head was in his hands, his elbows on the table.

'It may or may not surprise you,' he said at last, his voice muffled, 'but I love that bloody woman. I can't help myself, Jemma. She's under my skin and she knows it.' His head came up and his face was pale. 'The last thing in the world I want to do is divorce her. I don't want to lose her any more than I want to lose my daughter. She knows that, which is why she keeps taunting me with it. This latest allegation about us is just a part of it.'

'And,' Jemma whispered, 'I love Arne, Dave, more than I'll ever be able to say. I don't want to lose him to—to Johanna, or any woman!'

Her watch told her that it was late and that she ought to go. But Dave still seemed to need her moral support and encouragement. She couldn't leave him yet. He drained his cup and held his head again and from somewhere inside her she dredged soothing words to calm him down, wishing she could draw comfort from them, too.

It was half an hour before midnight when the telephone rang. Jemma, being the nearest, answered it, the action coming naturally from the past. Saying her name and number, again automatically, she realised her mistake. There was an intake of breath, followed by high-pitched, near-hysterical laughter.

'I don't believe it, I just don't believe it,' Johanna's voice said shrilly. 'All I wanted to know was whether my husband ever intends to live at home again. And what do I get? The silvery tones of his mistress!'

'Johanna,' Jemma cried, 'listen to me...'

But Johanna wasn't in the mood to listen to anyone. 'Arne, darling, do you want to speak to your oh-so-faithful wife? She's here, on the other end of the line, in the flat she's leased to my *faithful* husband. At this time of night, Arne! And only the other day she tried to deny there was anything between them! Can you believe that?'

The phone changed hands. Arne's voice came loud, clear and harsh. 'Jemma?'

She could not bring herself to answer, mauling her lip and crying silent tears. Her own unthinking action in answering the call had condemned her even more in Arne's eyes.

'*Jemma!*' The anger in that single word almost sent her reeling.

'Here, give me that,' Dave exclaimed. 'I'll put him right on the matter once and for all. And tell him what I think of him for enticing my wife and child away from me.' He tore the receiver from Jemma. 'Arne? For God's sake, man——'

There was a slam from the other end, then nothing. Dave looked at the silent telephone, then abandoned it, walking up and down, running shaking fingers through his hair.

'So he refuses to listen. Just where does this get us, Jemma?'

Mechanically, she started clearing away, then stopped, staring through the uncurtained window into the outer darkness. A picture formed of Arne's face, his intensely blue eyes, the smile he wore after they had made love and they were still bound intimately to each other.

Her breathing grew heavy as another image flashed into focus: of Johanna on the receiving end of that smile, Johanna lying in Arne's arms, the baby they had created happily asleep in the next room... She gasped at the pain the picture produced.

'I'm going to have to move out, Dave,' she said in a choked voice. 'Away from Arne. I couldn't bring myself to live with him any more, knowing he preferred another woman in his life. Johanna told me more than once that he'd married me for expediency, not love. I suppose I have finally to accept that what she said is true.'

There was a short silence and Dave raised a haggard face. 'What do you plan to do?'

With her fingertips she smoothed the polished table top. It was hers, just as the flat was hers. 'Would you object if I——?'

'Moved in here? How could I object? It's yours. I'll find somewhere else.'

'Surely there's no need, Dave. There are two bedrooms.'

He frowned. 'You're being a bit naïve, aren't you, Jemma? You know what living here with me would lead to. Confirmation in Arne's eyes—not to mention Johanna's—that we do have a relationship. And there'd be gossip, rampant rumour, people staring. I'm talking about our place of work.'

Jemma gave a ragged sigh. 'I've already denied it to Arne, and he refused to believe me. Johanna's just confirmed it as a certainty—or so she'll claim—by that phone call this evening. You tried to put things straight with Arne, yet look what he did—hung up on you. He just didn't want to know. And,' her head lifted high, 'we both know it's not true that we're having an affair, anyway. Which should make it easier for us to take the gossip in our stride.'

For a few moments, Dave considered the situation. 'It's your choice, Jemma,' he said at last. 'And your flat.' His smile was faint. 'Your company certainly wouldn't be unwelcome.'

'Thanks for that, Dave. It'll take me a few days to organise my private affairs. I'll let you know when I'm coming.'

He nodded, slowly loosening his tie. He suppressed a heavy yawn, then shivered as though he was cold. Jemma saw how fatigued he was. His heavy work-load, plus his private life being in disarray, was working on him like a virus, tunnelling under his well-being.

It wouldn't be long, she guessed by her experience with others, before his whole world began to collapse beneath him. And if Johanna ever broke the news to him that the little girl he loved so much was not his after all, but was the child of her affair with Arne, he would go down with his crumbling world and be engulfed by it.

No, she acknowledged secretly, whatever the cost to herself in the way of reputation, she knew she didn't have the heart to turn Dave out of the flat he now seemed to regard as his home.

In her husband's estimation, she had already faced the fact that her integrity was less than the dust beneath his feet. So she didn't have anything to lose in that direction, did she?

Other people's troubles masked her own for the next day or so. The evening before, she had started packing her belongings into cases and boxes, taking only those items that she would personally need. At the flat, many of her possessions remained from before her marriage, awaiting that 'time to spare' that had never seemed to materialise.

As she had surveyed her handiwork, then sank on to the bed, a sense of hopelessness had swept over her. It all seemed so final, the step she was taking in leaving Arne's house irrevocable. Because by doing so, she was also leaving Arne, leaving her marriage—and the father of her coming child.

No, no, she thought, tears thick in her throat, he's the one who's left our marriage, left it for the woman he really loves and the child whose reason for existence in this world they shared.

Idly next morning, she played with a large metal paper clip. Compressing its powerful spring, she watched its jaws open and close, experiencing a faint sense of satisfaction as its pointed teeth met and snapped.

What advice, she mused, was she was constantly giving her clients? That where their problems were concerned, they should fight and fight again for what they believed was right—*and never give up hope*.

Seizing the internal phone, Jemma dialled Dave's extension.

'I think he might have gone,' his secretary answered. 'I'll just check. Oh, good. He's here, after all. Mrs Drummond for you, Mr Forrest. OK if I go now?'

'Yes, go,' came faintly from the receiver, then, 'Well, Jemma?'

The question came so eagerly, it almost broke her heart. She had no news to pass on to him about his little daughter, which he was probably hoping for.

'Just this, Dave. I've come to a decision. I'm not the sort to be walked over by anyone, let alone by someone who's blatantly out to steal what's truly mine.' She sketched a doodle on her scratch pad.

'A doormat, Jemma, is something you certainly are not.'

'Right. So I'm going to fight for him, Dave. I refuse to let that bitch of a wife of yours—forgive me, but at this moment she's my sworn enemy—take the man I love from me. You do understand how I feel?'

'One hundred per cent comprehension, Jemma.'

'Thanks for that. I may need a couple of days off. Do you mind? I'll postpone my appointments——'

'A couple of days is fine by me. I'll be going away myself shortly. Business deal abroad.' A pause, then with a catch in his throat, 'Good luck, Jemma—for both our sakes.'

Next day, Jemma saw a selected number of clients, dealing only with urgent cases. Then it was lunch time, her diary by then bearing a series of crossings out through times and names.

With Cindy's help, she had managed to cancel meetings, alter dates of visits and find an ex-colleague from a previous job to take over the problems that couldn't wait.

It was mid-afternoon by the time she set out in her car. Hurriedly, she had pushed some personal items, plus a few changes of clothes, into a zipped bag. If it took her all week, she would oust that woman Johanna from Arne's arms and Arne's life.

This time she knew the way without having to ask for help. It grew darker as she approached the coast, the clouds forming into a heavy, rain-threatening mass overhead. Braking to a halt in the parking area, she noted that hers was one with only two other cars—Arne's, and another which she recognised as Johanna's.

Which meant, Jemma thought, her heart jolting, that Johanna was still with him. Her resolve almost foundered, her fingers gripping the steering-wheel.

Brutally, she forced herself to divorce reality from the dream that had danced in front of her eyes for the whole of the journey—of Arne greeting her alone, his face lighting up, his arms opening wide and closing around her as she ran into them.

Now face facts, she told herself severely. What assets did she personally possess that, where Arne was concerned, gave her an advantage over Johanna Forrest? None, she told herself. Not even the baby she was expecting, the start of the family Arne had told her he had wanted so much, would interest him now—after all, he had one of his own, didn't he?—the little girl called Tracey, by the woman who had gone back to him.

Hadn't Johanna confirmed it in the course of her tormenting outburst? So what if Arne, before his attention was distracted, had started to deny the child was his? He would reject such a claim, wouldn't he, with his wife looking on and hearing every giveaway statement Johanna made?

Or maybe she had just that minute confessed the truth to Arne? Maybe he hadn't until that moment known Tracey was his and not Dave's, after all? She remembered the shock on his face as Johanna had made the claim. Or had it been surprise?

Lifting her head, she stared defiantly at the dark shape that was Arne's place. 'Well, this time,' she told herself, 'I'm going to *make* him believe me instead of Johanna. I'm not leaving here until he accepts the truth—that there's nothing between Dave and myself.'

Tugging her bag from the rear seat, she locked the car and picked her way carefully along the road until it lost itself in the sands of the beach.

The sea was noisy and wild, and its sounds filled Jemma's head with a primitive fear. The spray of the breaking waves showered over her as she began to climb the slope to the cottage. The wind had risen, whipping around her. Longingly, she thought of the warm coat she had so foolishly left in the car. The three-quarter moon had slid behind the clouds and there was scarcely enough light left to see more than a foot or two ahead.

There was no answer to her knock. Trying again, she received only silence in reply. He must be there, she argued. Lights were on, upstairs and down. She felt a lurch of dread inside her. Had they put the little girl to bed, and gone to Arne's room—*to make love?*

Starting to shiver now, with cold and fear and hope-lessness, she left her bag on the doorstep and turned to pick her way down the slope to fetch her coat from the car. Somehow she would have to find sufficient warmth to stop this awful trembling.

The sea roared, the darkness closed in, cloaking everything but a pace or two in front. There were loose pieces of rock, she remembered, and dips in the ground. For better balance, she thrust her arms wide.

To the left the land rose to form the higher ground on which the cottage stood. To the right the shallow cliff dropped away to meet the shore, while at its base the sea threw the remnants of the rolling waves. The tide, she guessed, had not quite reached its highest point.

In her haste to get started on her journey, she had forgotten to change out of her sandals. Now, she re-gretted her forgetfulness. Her feet began to slide on the damp surface created by the seaspray. It was a rough stone that finally threw her off balance.

Clawing madly at the air, she made a desperate attempt to right herself, losing the battle and falling headlong over the slope, bouncing on hip and thigh, finally sliding to a stop...feeling the sand's cold dampness on her legs only seconds before her head came into sharp, agonising contact with a boulder, blacking out the world.

She felt she was floating, thought the waves had claimed her at last. The baby, she thought, oh God, I don't want to lose the baby... Strong arms were lifting her, carrying her with care and haste. Any moment now, she would sink to the bottom of the ocean, rising again as a piece of drowned flotsam on Arne's beach.

The irony of it, she thought, wanting to smile, but her lips were too stiff to oblige. I, Jemma Drummond, picked up by my husband, the great Armin Power, to be fashioned by him into a piece of sculpture for display in his exhibition...

'Jemma!' Like a distant voice from outer space, the word teased her ear. It was spoken through teeth that seemed to be clenched—whether with anxiety or anger, it was impossible in her dazed state to decide.

It came again, and someone was compressing her chest, then releasing it, breathing into her mouth—giving her the kiss of life?

'Jemma...' A warning this time, to stop being foolish, return to the living, or else...

It was easier now to breathe, but there was a terrible pain somewhere in her body. Her head throbbed and her limbs ached. Better to relax, her common sense advised, and drift away in someone's strong arms...

Voices faded in and out across the thin line of her awareness. There was the sound of hustle, a child's irritable cries, a man's voice comforting, then silence.

It was so much easier, Jemma found, to slip back into the void she had been in since that rock had sent her spinning like a top to the bottom of that cliff. Before she slid back into unconsciousness, the thought hit her again: Oh God, I hope...oh, I do hope I haven't lost the baby...

Voices again, different this time, with urgency and authority. Someone was saying her name. 'Mrs Drummond, how do you feel? You've had a nasty bump, haven't you?'

Jemma tried to nod, but the movement was too painful, so she moved her lips, saying, 'Yes,' adding, 'I'm fine...I think.'

There was sympathetic laughter and Jemma knew at that moment that there was something very important that she had to ask. Her eyes fluttered open and she whispered to the nurse who was bending over her.

'The baby, is the baby all right?'

The nurse took her hand which lay listlessly on the bed. Slowly her head moved from side to side. 'I'm sorry, dear. We did our best...'

Jemma's eyes closed and her hand tightened into a fist as the nurse replaced it gently on the bedcover. She wished she could slide back into oblivion, she wished she could turn back the clock and begin her journey to Arne's cottage all over again.

CHAPTER TEN

'WHY didn't you tell me you were pregnant?'

The nurse had gone. Arne's face, aloof and cold, met Jemma's fluttering glance. Despite her aches and pains, her heartbeats quickened. It was so good to see him again.

He was leaner, somehow, his navy knitted shirt moulding to pulled-back shoulders. His bare, tanned arms were folded, hips muscled, his stance wide-paced. There were secret shadows in his face, his upper lip and jaw dark as if the razor had made only fleeting contact.

His attitude puzzled her. How should she interpret his strangely withdrawn manner? As annoyance that she had—as he saw it—kept her pregnancy a secret from him, or anger that she had been so careless as to lose the child?

She had an overpowering desire to touch him. If they could make physical contact, she was sure all their troubles would melt away. If only he would bend down and brush her lips with his... But this man beside her bed was a stranger, although surely, even to a stranger, she could stretch out her hand?

He looked at it, lifted it and returned it to the bed. If he had noticed that the fingers trembled a little at his touch, it had not appeared to move him one bit. As a put-down, Jemma thought unhappily, it couldn't have been bettered.

How much more plainly could he have expressed his inclinations—that he no longer wanted anything to do with her, his wife? That the only woman he wanted in his life from that moment on was the one he had lost to another man two years before, but who was only too willing now to come back into it?

'I was going to tell you about the baby,' she said at last. 'It was why I came. I knocked. You didn't answer the door.' She sought his eyes, hoping for a spark, finding only dead embers.

'I was working in my studio,' he answered. 'It's a converted barn, away from the cottage. Something made me leave my work and go round to the front entrance door——'

'Where you saw my bag, on the step.'

'Thank God I did. You cried out for help. Which was how I knew where to look.'

Discovering what had happened to her, how had he felt? Nothing in his face gave his feelings away.

'How can I thank you, Arne, for saving my life?'

He said nothing, just looked down at her. Wasn't he experiencing the slightest regret at their mutual loss, nor even feeling some sympathy for her? Hadn't she, after all, just lost part of herself, *part of them both?*

What was he thinking? She wanted so badly to talk to him, to hold out her arms, inviting his kiss, finding comfort and solace in his embrace... Hear him say, 'Never mind, darling, we can always try again...'

It seemed he wasn't even able any longer to read the message in her eyes... Had he no feelings for her at all any more? Would she never find the way back to his public self, let alone the very private side of him? Her head turned restlessly on the pillow.

'Did Dave know?'

Jemma frowned, uncomprehending.

'About the child you were expecting,' he enlarged.

'No. Why should he?'

'Every reason, I should have thought.'

Her brain, functioning sluggishly under the influence of the medication she had received, took a few moments to follow the path of his reasoning.

She closed her eyes, a feeling of desperate tiredness hitting her. He was attributing the baby she had been expecting to Dave! But why? She found the answer at once. As a means of vindicating himself from the part he played in Tracey's birth. Also, to justify his own resumed affair with Johanna, on the grounds that she, Jemma, was deeply into a relationship with Johanna's husband. The poison Johanna had poured into his ear had done its deadly work.

What could she say to him to make him accept that he had got it all wrong? What kind of words could she use to persuade him that not only had the child she had lost irrefutably been his, but that she had stayed faithful to him all the time they had been apart?

If he wanted Johanna and not her, his wife, would cold reason and honest speaking reach him? Of course not, she told herself. He wouldn't allow anything to penetrate his defences, would he? Should she even try?

'The baby was yours and mine, Arne, not Dave's.'

The curtains around the bed moved agitatedly. Johanna came through, holding Tracey. 'I heard everything she's said, and she's lying, Arne,' Johanna hissed, her voice low. 'I rang Dave because of the way she kept saying "Tell Dave, tell Dave——"'

'I don't believe you,' Jemma exclaimed.

'Oh yes, you did. Didn't she, Arne?' He nodded. 'When Arne carried you up to the cottage, you kept repeating it. And you kept talking about "the baby", too, which is how we guessed. And put two and two together.'

Johanna's slim body was encased in white, the jumpsuit drawn in at the waist with a gilt-linked chain, the metal finding an echo in the real gold of the rings on her scarlet-tipped fingers, the provocative circles swinging at her ears, the glint of gold in her almond-shaped eyes.

Gold bangles enhanced the slender arms that held her child, an echo of herself in looks, as if she were also a jewel to be proud of.

'What I must have meant about Dave,' Jemma said, drawing dryness into her throat from a parched mouth, 'was to tell him I'd be away longer than I said. That he'd have to find someone to take my place at work.'

'Oh, really?' The sarcasm twisted Johanna's perfectly shaped mouth. 'So why did Dave tell me you were going to move in with him when you got back?' Her eyes flashed in triumph and she pushed Tracey's chubby hand from her chin.

Oh God, Jemma thought, why did Dave tell her that? The answer was obvious, wasn't it? Loving his wife as he had confessed, he had wanted to make her jealous!

'Is this true, Jemma?' Arne asked tersely.

'It's true.' What else could she do, once again, but admit it? Because it was the truth. Like Dave's head against her breast, her arms cradling him and giving comfort had been the truth. To the unsuspicious mind, all on the level, but fuel for the fire to anyone who wanted to make trouble.

And once again, Johanna had had every intention of fuelling an emotional upheaval between her, Jemma, and Arne. Once again, she had succeeded, using the truth out of context in order to prove her own case.

Arne's eyes iced over and Jemma shivered despite the warmth of the bedclothes. He had accepted Johanna's statements at face value!

'So be honest, Mrs Drummond,' Johanna gloated. 'Whose baby was it? *Your* husband's or *mine*?'

Three days later, Jemma was allowed to leave the hospital. Her bones ached, the pain from the bumps and bruises scattered over her body making her flesh throb with every movement she made.

In their own good time and Nature's, the doctors told her, they would heal. What those doctors didn't know was that the searing ache deep in her heart would never go away.

There was no reason, they had reassured her, why, one day when her body had recovered from the loss of the baby, she and her husband should not try again. What they also didn't know, and she would never tell them, was that she and her husband were drifting irrevocably apart, in totally opposite directions. The word 'divorce' haunted her sleep, turning her dreams into nightmares.

That was, when she could sleep... which was rare, because of the intense discomfort of her injuries, and the dull pain in her heart.

When Arne had driven her to his cottage and carried her inside, Johanna had been standing on the doorstep, looking every inch the owner's wife, mother of his child, and reluctant hostess to the invalid he was bringing into their home. 'I belong here,' her proprietorial attitude was saying, '*you* are the visitor, the interloper in Arne Drummond's life.'

The cottage had two bedrooms, one plainly intended for Arne's use and one which, it seemed, Johanna and

Tracey occupied. The question was—and Jemma did not really want to find the answer—whose room was more often shared, Tracey's or Arne's?

When Arne had carried Jemma upstairs, lowering her with an aloof gentleness on to the double bed, she had declared, 'I'm not sleeping with you, Arne. A sofa downstairs will suit me fine.'

His eyebrows had lifted, his eyes as cold as the grey sea beyond the nearby shore. 'Do you honestly believe,' he said, his tone stinging, 'that I'm the kind of man who would want to share his bed with a wife whose only reason for visiting him was to tell him she was expecting another man's child?'

What use would it be, she asked herself, to deny yet again that Johanna's allegations had no foundation? All her twisted reasoning had been based on what appeared superficially to be the truth.

The nights were the worst. For three of them she tossed and turned, longing for Arne's arms around her, wearying for the first glimmer of daylight, then lying there listening to the wash of the sea, the keening, early morning cry of the seagulls.

On the fourth night, in the early hours, she found that she could not stand her own restlessness another moment. Getting out of bed, she donned a fine blue cotton robe which Arne had found in her bag. Clinging to the stair rail, she made her way down, swaying a little as she walked.

It was her first time up and faintness threatened. A half opened door revealed the whereabouts of the kitchen. Thankfully, she slumped into a wooden chair, looking with longing at the fridge. If she could make it across the room, she would probably find milk there which she could warm.

With a gigantic effort, she got to her feet. Giddiness caught up with her and she crumpled, the stone floor hard and icy against her skin. The shaking started—reaction and shock combined—and she could not stop it.

The outer door was thrown open and Arne burst in, his mood as dark as the night outside. 'Johanna,' he said, 'I saw the light. Is it Tracey?' When he saw Jemma, he seemed turned to stone. But not for long. Three strides brought him to her.

'For God's sake, Jemma——' Was his voice shaking a little? Hands raised her, caught her to a hard male frame.

She was swung into arms of iron, every bone in her body jarring as she was carried into another room. In the air was the wispy smell of woodsmoke, lingering after a fire had died down. The sofa she was lowered to felt soft and well used, but the thighs and chest supporting her that had intervened between herself and the upholstery had grown as unfamiliar during the passing of the weeks as those of a stranger.

Her arms, recovered from the trembling that had assailed her, acted as if they had a will of their own, seeking out the sturdiness of the torso her eager hands had once known by heart. Discovering it back in her possession released inside her a surge of emotion whose overwhelming strength swept her helplessly along in its relentless path.

It began with a choking sob and the tears, once started, shook her still-tender frame. They poured down her cheeks, dampening the rough sweater Arne wore. She clung, she could not help it, her fingertips digging into his shoulder blades, her head pressing against his ribs.

She cried for all that she had lost, a husband, a friend, a tender lover; a child which he—and as she had discovered, she—had wanted so much. A life of love and laughter forfeited for a future that was bleak and empty, with work the only solace.

He let her cry, his hold on her never wavering. From the jungle of her emotions, the intensity of her distress, the thought broke its way through: I was wrong. I'm the one he loves, not Johanna...

'I'm sorry.' She raked for a handkerchief in her pocket, only to find one pushed into her hand. She used it, then it was taken from her and put away. Avoiding Arne's eyes, she pushed at her tumbled hair, pressed her burning cheeks with the backs of her hands.

Her heartbeats were racing. Now he would say it— wouldn't he? 'Come back to me, Jemma, and we'll create another child... I can't live without you...'

He lifted her aside, getting to his feet and pocketing his hands. 'I didn't realise,' he commented darkly, 'that the loss of Dave's child would affect you so deeply. If he means that much to you, I'll get him here. Just say the word.'

Staring up at him, she felt anger stain her cheeks, mixing with the already overheated blood. 'Dave means nothing to me, nothing!'

His shoulders lifted non-committally, his eyes still below zero. 'So you've been indulging in an affair, and were careless. Was it the coming child that made you decide to move out of my house and in with him, making the relationship more permanent?'

'My house', he had said! So in his eyes, it was no longer hers to share.

'All I wanted,' she asserted, struggling to her feet, the strength of her anger reduced by fatigue, 'was a warm drink to help me sleep.' The effort of rising was too much and she fell back to the softness of the sofa.

Arne heated some milk and while Jemma drank it, stared through the window at the lightening sky.

'Arne? Where do you sleep?' she asked at last, putting aside the empty mug.

'In my studio. *When* I sleep. Most nights I work.'

He was facing her now, staring down at her. She saw the shadows, the hollows in his face she had never noticed before, the dark areas of stubble. He looked tired to death and it cut her to her heart's depths.

Lifting her arms, she stretched them towards him. Tears welled again at the intensity of her feelings, her need to hold him, soothe him, to drive away his fatigue.

A strange expression passed over his face, and he muttered words which Jemma could not catch. Then, as if he couldn't help himself he bent towards her. She was in his arms again, being carried up the stairs, in her face a shining joy.

The bedside light threw a shaded glow over the cream and grey of his room. In a dream, she drew off the cotton robe and watched with wonder as he tugged free of his shirt.

Instead of pulling the covers over her, he turned them back and extinguished the lamp. A few moments later, Jemma felt him beside her, the bedcovers over them, his bare skin bringing her flesh to pounding life.

He turned her away from him, wrapped his arms around her breasts beneath her nightgown and eased her back against his body. She knew he was aroused, felt his deep, steadying breaths, his pounding heartbeats, as if they were her own.

He asked nothing of her. Curled into him, the aching discomfort from her wounds which had for three nights tormented her receded under the influence of his warm, encompassing embrace. Her breasts had hardened under his touch—he must have noticed—her loins burning with a desire only he could arouse within her.

He went on holding her, his breathing slowing, his muscles relaxing; but his hold on her body stayed firm and possessive—and infinitely tender.

When she awoke, she didn't even care what time it was. Turning, arms reaching out, she found only an empty place, the warmth of his body still lingering. There were sounds downstairs of breakfast, Tracey's peeved cry for something that was being denied her.

I know how she feels, Jemma thought, stretching her limbs into the place where Arne had lain. It couldn't have been long since he had left her. If only, she thought, I'd woken just a little earlier . . . All night he'd held her, making no demands.

Rolling on to her back, she hugged herself, smiling at the memories of the night. He had stroked her body while she slept, kissed her shoulders, turned her face with a feather's touch and kissed her softly, lingeringly, as if his lips were drinking deep after long waterless days in a desert.

Surfacing from her dreams, she had turned into him and kissed him back, but sleep had claimed her again and reality had melted once more into fantasy, until she had not been able to work out how much was real, and how much imagined.

But she was sure she hadn't imagined it. It was Arne's way, having discovered that he still loved her, of telling her so.

The door opened and her bright smile was there to greet Arne's return. Except that it wasn't Arne.

'So,' said Johanna, closing the door and keeping an indignant Tracey outside, 'you persuaded Arne to sleep with you. It was a clever trick—but it didn't work! He was sorry for you, that's all.' She regarded Jemma narrowly. 'I bet all he did was comfort you. I bet he didn't make love.'

Jemma cursed whatever it was that had appeared unwittingly in her face, putting malice into Johanna's smile.

'Not only that,' she went on, '*I* know that he's got one great big guilt complex about you. Ever since your accident—and that was neatly done, too, wasn't it, so dramatic and touching!—he's been cursing himself for being the cause of it.'

Carefully, Jemma locked away the memories of Arne's loving embrace in the darkness. Nothing must touch them, nor spoil them. She would not allow Johanna's acid comments to corrode them.

'Guilt complex?' Jemma queried. 'Why? It wasn't Arne's fault that I slipped and fell.'

'It was Dave's child, wasn't it? Arne feels guilty about not hearing you knock the day you arrived.'

It was time, Jemma decided, more than time that she put Johanna right once and for all on the subject of the father of the child she, Jemma, had lost. Reaching for the cotton robe, Jemma put it on, pushing back the bedclothes and swinging her legs round.

'Johanna,' she said, 'you have to believe me—it was *not* Dave's baby. It was Arne's.'

'You're lying! How could it have been Arne's? I know for certain he hasn't lived with you for weeks. I've been here for most of that time, which proves it.'

'Acting as his model, I suppose?' Even as Jemma spoke, she cursed the giveaway question, even filled as it had been with sarcasm.

Johanna clasped her hands and gave a rapturous smile. 'That. And—er—other things.'

'So where were you,' Jemma challenged, 'the night he came all the way back home to be with me? We made love, Johanna, *all night long.*'

'That—that——' The question, and the statement that followed it, seemed to have floored her. But only momentarily. 'That particular weekend I took Tracey to see her grandmother. Which means Arne was missing me, and wanted me. I wasn't here, and as we both know,' she gave a small, brittle smile, 'being all man, he got desperate and had to make do with you. He left you again next morning, didn't he? I know, because I came back early, and he was here.'

This entire conversation's pointless, Jemma concluded wearily.

'Even if Arne did sleep with you,' Johanna affirmed, 'it doesn't prove the child you were expecting was his. I *know* you're in the middle of an affair with Dave. You see, I also know how much he admires you.'

She took a step or two towards Jemma, her hands moving agitatedly.

'At that party I gave and you and Arne came to,' she went on, 'and even at your own wedding reception, Dave couldn't keep away from you. I watched him push towards you through the crowd like a moth to a flame. Do you think I didn't notice?'

Jemma remembered the curiously determined way Dave, on each occasion, had made his way to her side, standing there, lifeless in face and manner, letting her do the talking and scarcely replying. Yet he had stood there, as if that, in all the world, was where he had wanted to be. Was it any wonder that his wife believed that she, Jemma, attracted him?

Wasn't it true, too, that with her, Dave wasn't deadpan any more? That somehow, without even trying, she

struck sparks inside him? So what did that mean? Very
little, really. In spite of all Johanna's accusations, it still
didn't add up to anything more than a warm friendship,
an understanding between them that went beyond words.

Jemma shook her head, endeavouring to put Johanna
right, but the other woman was in no mood to listen to
reason.

'You have some strange effect on him,' Johanna in-
sisted again. 'There's a light in his eyes when he talks
to you. It's never there for me. He—he looks at me
sometimes as if he'd—he'd like to choke me. But you—
you have some sort of power over him that does the
opposite. He's like a statue come to life.'

I can't believe it, Jemma thought, staring at her bare
toes digging into the pink pile of the bedside rug. Her
brain had started working again, her counselling self
rising to the surface as, to her astonishment and disbelief,
comprehension dawned. Johanna Forrest, in her own
proud and coded way, was asking for help, for advice,
for professional guidance. *Because her marriage was
foundering, almost sunk without trace*...

What can I do? Jemma thought. How can I help? By
telling her the truth.

'Dave loves you, Johanna,' she offered quietly. 'He
told me so himself.'

The revelation seemed to have the opposite effect.

'So he's been discussing me with you, has he?'
Johanna exclaimed, anger bathing the smooth skin of
her face with scarlet. 'Which shows just how *intimate*
you are with him. While you were making love,' she
sneered, 'did he say, "I love you, Johanna", forgetting
as he was swept away by unbridled passion that he was
holding you in his arms and not me, and mixing up our
names?'

There was a fretful cry from the other side of the door. 'Mummy come,' Tracey called. 'Want Mummy!'

Johanna glanced at the door, then turned back to Jemma. 'So Dave loves me, does he? Why hasn't he told me—*me*?' Her fingertips, touching her chest, held the faintest tremble. 'He hasn't, so I don't believe it.' Her smile widened her almost perfect mouth. 'But Arne's told me,' she went on, 'in the most flattering way possible. It's the greatest compliment an artist can pay a woman. He's created this sculpture. It's magnificent, it's the work of a genius, like I said. He's covered it over, it's not for public eyes until the exhibition opens. But *I* know there's a woman in it, and her face, he told me, is the face of the woman he loves most in the world. Guess who, *Mrs Drummond*,' Johanna gloated, 'guess whose face the woman has?'

'You've seen it?' Jemma's heart sank, the question a mere whisper. 'The face is yours?'

Johanna clasped her hands and closed her eyes. 'It's really something,' she murmured, 'it's beautiful, it's a work of art. It repays me for all the hours I've posed for him, the public relations work I've done. Not to mention all the——' her eyes slid sideways, taunting Jemma, 'intimate moments we've shared...'

From across the room, the telephone shrilled. Jemma stared at it, wondering whether she should make the physical effort to answer it. Johanna stared, too, as if it had come alive and was threatening her.

'Will Arne take the call?' Jemma queried, as the ringing went on.

'He's in his studio. There's no extension there.' Slowly, as if hypnotised, Johanna went towards it, picking it up and listening.

'Arne?' a man's voice was saying. 'Are you there?'

Johanna took a breath and spoke to her husband. 'Sorry to disappoint you,' she said unpleasantly, 'but he's busy.'

'That's OK,' Jemma heard him reply, his voice coming over clearly, almost as if he were pleased to be talking to his wife. 'That's fine. How are you, Johanna?' He waited for a reply that did not come. 'How's Tracey?'

'You'd like to know, wouldn't you?' Johanna answered. 'You'd really like to know. Well, I'm not telling you. She's my child, Dave, and I——'

Oh God, Jemma thought, she's not going to tell him the truth now about the paternity of her child? That he, Dave, is not the true father...

'How's Jemma?' he broke in, long-suffering patience mixing with disappointment at his wife's belligerence. But he didn't know, did he, the awful revelation he had been spared. For how long? Jemma wondered sadly. Which moment would Johanna choose to drop the bombshell?

'That's why you phoned in the first place, isn't it?' Johanna taunted. 'You didn't really want to speak to Arne. Why weren't you honest enough to say so at the start? You want to know how your *woman* is? Then I'll *give* her to you.'

She tossed the receiver on to the bed and stormed out. Jemma reached for it and grasped it, without having to walk round the bed. Which, she reflected, surprised, was a thoughtful gesture on Johanna's part, even if it was ungraciously made.

'Hi, Dave,' Jemma said, pity for him softening her tone. 'I'm feeling better, thanks. A little each day. Dave, I'm sorry about being away from work for so long. Who's tackling the problems? Have you managed to get a stand-in for me? All those people I've had to let down who needed my help——'

'Don't you worry yourself, Jemma,' Dave assured her. 'Your ex-colleague's doing fine. She's taken some leave from her own job, and started here where you left off. So you can rest your pretty head contentedly each night.' He paused. 'What are your plans now?'

'Personal plans, you mean? For the future?'

She knew why he had asked. Was there any chance, he was saying silently, of the affair between my wife and your husband coming to an end? Well, she thought sadly, she was going to have to disappoint him.

'I can't see any reason to alter them, Dave. My mind hasn't been changed by—events here.'

She could almost see the disappointment in his face.

'Right . . .' He seemed to need to think about the situation. 'I'll probably be away when you arrive. I'm due to fly to Italy any day. Jemma,' he seemed to need to take a breath, 'why didn't you tell me you were pregnant?'

'I didn't want to worry you, that's why. You had your own troubles. And,' she played with the connecting cord, her back to the door, 'I thought the first person to be told about the baby should be its father. I intended telling you when I got back.'

There was a movement in the doorway. Arne stood there, arms folded. Jemma's heart turned over. How much had he heard? There was thunder in his face, lightning in his eyes. As Jemma stared at him, it forked towards her and struck her. She winced at the pain, at the contempt in the set of his jaw, the cynicism in the slashed line of his mouth.

Had he misunderstood her last words to Dave, interpreting them as absolute confirmation that Dave was the father of the child she had lost? If only, she thought, I'd spoken them in reverse order!

'When Arne called me,' Dave went on, having no means of knowing the conversation was being over-heard by the person in question, 'and told me what had happened to you…what had nearly happened to you…I nearly died. You kept saying my name, he said. Why, Jemma?' His tone had softened, full of expectation.

She had to tell him the truth at once, especially with Arne standing beside her, listening to every word. 'I was worried about my work, Dave. I wanted you to know I wouldn't be back when I said.'

'Ah.' One word, but expressing comprehension and, Jemma wondered, just a little relief? It was plain that Arne had not caught the slight lessening of tension in Dave's voice.

'I might be here for a few days, yet, Dave,' Jemma said. 'Could you ask Cindy to put together any papers that need my attention and put them in the post? I could work on them here——'

The receiver was taken from her and she looked up at Arne with astonishment.

'It won't be necessary, Dave,' he said briskly. 'We're all leaving here in a few days. Jemma should be fit enough by then.' His glance flicked her like a whip. 'The exhibition's in a couple of weeks. At Johanna's father's gallery in London. I'm arranging transport for my work. I have to oversee that, then we'll be leaving.'

They exchanged a few more words, businesslike on Dave's side, terse on Arne's, and disconnected.

Arne shot her a look of the deepest contempt. If he saw her trembling lip, it did not seem to touch him. Without a word, he swung on his heel and left.

His unforgiving attitude tore Jemma apart. After his warmth in the night, she could hardly bear the pain of his rejection now.

In her thoughts, she unlocked the door on the night's tender memories, her eyes filling with tears as, one by one, she let them fly away.

CHAPTER ELEVEN

THE journey home was behind them. It had been a silent one for much of the time, for which Jemma had been thankful, brief snatches of impersonal small talk having been interspersed with taped music or discussions on the car radio.

Facing each other, they stood in the living-room. For Jemma, it had been an anguished homecoming. We may be together again, she thought, but we're farther apart than ever. Arne was staring at her like a man who had climbed a mountain and was looking at last on the panorama he had laboured so hard to see. But the mist must have come down and blotted out the view. His expression clouded over, the light in his eyes dying completely away.

He's been looking for Johanna in my face, Jemma despaired, but found only me—the wrong woman.

'Isn't it great to be back, Arne?' she remarked, making a determined effort to bridge the chasm that yawned between them.

'Is it?' His eyes swung to the boxes stacked in a corner, the ones she had packed to take to her apartment. 'I wasn't totally convinced that you really meant what you said about moving in with Forrest until I saw those. Now I know you did.'

She had to make one more attempt to put him right about that. 'Arne, I wasn't moving in with him in the sense you mean.'

His wide shoulders lifted. 'Moving in with him, living with him? Where's the difference? Dave's away, isn't he?'

Jemma nodded. 'So don't fall over yourself rushing to cut loose from me. I won't be sleeping here until the exhibition's over.'

'You'll be sleeping at Johanna's instead.' The accusing statement had burst from her unawares. Had part of her hoped for a denial? Just how ingenuous could she get?

'At Johanna's and Dave's London apartment, yes. It's convenient for the Oceanic Gallery where the exhibition's taking place.'

I bet it is, Jemma thought with a bitterness that burned, and for other things, too. Those 'intimate moments', for instance, that he and Johanna shared. Would their daughter be there, also, to complete the family picture?

'Johanna's taking Tracey to her mother's.'

Which neatly answered her question. How cosy it would be, Jemma thought acidly, just the two of them, sleeping together at night, travelling to the gallery together in the mornings, greeting Johanna's father, the owner, hand in hand, probably...

Jemma shrugged. 'So, since Dave's not back yet, I might as well delay my move.'

Had she hurt him as much as he was hurting her? She couldn't tell, but his fine mouth twisted with a contempt that squeezed her inside to screaming pitch. What good is it doing, she reproached herself, scoring points off him? It only destroys me, too, and drives us farther apart.

He seemed to be about to leave. She wanted to run across and hang on to him, like a drowning swimmer grasping a slipping lifeline.

At the door he paused. 'You'll receive an invitation to the show's opening. Accept it or turn it down, it's your choice.'

Accept it, and find myself looking on the face of the woman you truly love? she almost shrieked. To gaze on the beautiful features of Johanna Forrest, the woman you adore?

'Thank you,' she said with a studied politeness which, she hoped, equalled his coolly calculated indifference. 'I'll do my best to attend. But you know how it is, my work's so demanding. So I'll make no promises.'

For one terrible moment she thought he was going to stride across and strike her. His piercing, merciless gaze did it for him. Listening to his footsteps crunching out to the driveway, she felt as shaken and shattered as if she had been savaged to within an inch of her life.

The art gallery was thronged with people. Jemma, on the edge of the crowd, had moved around in a kind of dream.

These beautiful works of art in front of her eyes, she kept reminding herself, had come from the hands of Armin Power, celebrated sculptor, known and admired all over the world. He was also Arne Drummond, her husband. This was the most unbelievable fact of all.

Even to Jemma's inexpert eyes, this man, this sculptor, was not just good, not merely gifted—his art bordered on the genius. It hurt unbearably that Johanna, his mistress, had recognised this, yet she, Jemma, his wife, had never even guessed it until now.

A growing excitement was raising the noise level. The time had almost come for the revelation of the *pièce de résistance,* the major sculpture around which the rest of the exhibition was designed.

Hidden by a white sheet, it stood centrally at one end of the long, colonnaded room. The unveiling ceremony, the programme notes explained—Johanna, as her father's public relations link, had almost certainly written them—would be performed by Johanna Forrest, the gallery owner's daughter.

With bitter eyes, Jemma sought out Johanna. She was talking animatedly to admiring listeners, her Grecian-style dress flowing around her shapely body, one white shoulder tantalisingly bare.

To one side of the shrouded sculpture, Arne stood thoughtfully, momentarily alone, hands in the pockets of his dress suit. He looked so handsome, so supremely confident and distinguished, Jemma's heart turned over.

His restless eyes clashed with hers. Around them, the voices, the laughter, the clinking glasses, faded away. They were on an island of silence, inhabited only by themselves. I love you, darling, she was crying inside, I always have and I always will... Couldn't he hear her, was he even trying? His eyes, cooling to zero, lifted to somewhere behind her. Deeply disappointed, she half turned.

'Jemma?' Dave stood just behind her. He had broken the spell. She was forced to make small talk, when all she really wanted to do was to run into her husband's arms...

Johanna had moved to stand beside the man the world knew as Armin Power, gazing into his eyes and capturing his entire attention.

'I made it, after all,' Dave was saying.

'That's good,' she answered automatically, then did a double-take. In his arms, his small daughter gazed wonderingly around.

'I collected her from my mother-in-law's as soon as I arrived back,' Dave explained, adding with a rare forcefulness, 'and from now on, I'm keeping her. If Johanna wants her, she'll have to take legal action and if she does, I'll declare war. I'm not letting my child go again without a fight.'

He kissed the chubby cheek, banishing the frown of bewilderment from the child's face.

And it was at that exact moment that Jemma discovered, beyond any shadow of a doubt, the true and indisputable identity of Tracey's father.

So she resembled her mother in her hair colour and the upper part of her face, but from the tip of her nose down, she was her father, beyond question. Side by side as those two faces now were, there was no mistaking Tracey's parentage. Dave Forrest had most certainly fathered his daughter. Johanna's claim that Tracey was Arne's was an outright lie!

Relief flooded Jemma's body. Turning to seek out Arne, the delight she felt at her discovery radiated from her. His eyes swung to meet hers and the flash of cold steel in them killed her new-found joy stone dead. He obviously believed that that joy arose from Dave Forrest's unexpected presence there.

'She looks so beautiful, Jemma.' Bewitched, Dave was staring at his wife. 'Tell me, for God's sake, how I can get her back.' He shifted Tracey into another position, caught Jemma's hand and pressed it desperately to his cheek. 'Counsel me, Jemma, advise me any way you like, in your professional capacity or as a dear friend. I don't want to fight my wife, not in the courts nor outside them. I just want her in my life and in my arms again. I'm begging you, Jemma—tell me what to do.'

*   *   *

'This man, this great artist, Armin Power,' Marcus Murdoch, dark-suited and grey-haired, was saying, 'a sculptor both traditional and modern...his rise in the world of sculpture being little short of meteoric, fantastic...his shapes, his forms, some of which need to be studied, maybe for years before their hidden messages work their way into our minds.'

Johanna stood at her father's side, but her flashing eyes were on the man about whom he was talking.

'Other works from his hands need no explanation—human truths reaching out to humankind, almost alarming in their power, with a suggestion of life itself exploding out of the stone in which he fashions his masterpieces.'

'Mummy come,' said Tracey loudly, her arm stretching hopefully in Johanna's direction. People nearby turned, smiling indulgently.

Johanna's eyes swung in the direction from which the clear young voice had come. Then they opened widely, colour creeping into her face, softening its lines as she saw who was holding her child in his arms. And it wasn't the colour of anger, Jemma noted abstractedly, more of...could it be shyness, mingled with pleasure?

'Bronze, wood, marble,' her father was saying, 'no matter what medium Armin Power might use, the ideas, the passions he's conveying delight the onlooker with their strength, their beauty and harmony...'

Any moment, Jemma remembered with a shock, the main subject of the exhibition would be revealed—and with it, Johanna's face, the true love in Armin Power's life. The woman surely wouldn't let the moment pass, Jemma was certain, without announcing that little titbit to the spectators, the world's press...and Dave!

I must get him out of here, Jemma thought. Her hand grasped Dave's shoulder.

'And now,' Marcus was saying with pride in his voice, 'I have great pleasure in asking my daughter, Johanna, to unveil——'

Arne's eyes reached out across the crowded room, fixing on Jemma's face. He seemed about to speak—to speak to *her*? Then he saw where her hand was resting. Swinging away, his brilliant eyes found Johanna, his smile warm and intimate.

'Dave,' Jemma urged, 'I have to speak to you. Now, this minute. Please!' Agitatedly, she urged his shoulder round towards the door. Johanna's voice rang out, 'I now have the greatest pleasure...'

They were in the corridor, the entrance lobby, then finally, with a smile at the security officer, in the street. Was this far enough away, Jemma wondered, to ensure that Dave didn't hear a single word of the public announcement that the wife he loved so much was also the adored lover of another man—the sculptor Armin Power, his ex-colleague, *his old friend*?

'You must tell her, Dave,' Jemma declared, eyes on the gallery entrance as if the world's press was about to erupt and demand a statement from them both. 'Your husband, madam, and your wife, sir, did you know they're——'

'Tell her what?' Dave was saying, giving an increasingly irritable Tracey a toy from his pocket.

'Everything you told me about your feelings for Johanna. That I mean absolutely nothing to you. That you love her, want her back——' Was he understanding at last? 'Somehow you must bridge the gap between you, with words, with actions, *with love*. I——'

She gave another anxious glance at the doorway.

'I'm advising you, Dave, as a counsellor, and as a woman. The first move's got to come from you. That's how I see it. I think—I'm almost sure—Johanna still has some feeling for you. It's a hunch I have from the things she said to me at Arne's cottage. Try it, try it for your own sake. And, Dave, try it for mine, too, will you? Please.'

The voices still rang in her head, the surprise, the praise, the admiration. They would not let her rest. The chimes of midnight from the grandfather clock downstairs hung in the air as she tried desperately to relax.

'My daughter Johanna,' the man was saying, 'this great work...indisputable evidence of the sculptor's love for her...telling mankind for centuries to come how much he adores my daughter...'

A sound dragged Jemma from the nightmare. She was not alone in the house! Certain that someone had broken in, she swung from the bed and crept down the stairs.

The intruder was in the living-room, walking about, knocking over a glass, cursing loudly. Jemma eased open the door, held her breath—and went cold. Arne had come home!

He had thrown himself into a low chair, minus jacket and tie. In the act of lifting his glass, he saw the dishevelled figure in the doorway. Taking his time, he finished off the drink, abandoning the glass. All the while, his relentless eyes continued raking her body, savouring every curve and indentation which, she realised too late, were clearly revealed beneath the thin nightgown.

'Still here?' he drawled with mock surprise. 'I'd have thought you'd have moved out by now and into Dave

Forrest's waiting arms. He seemed eager enough to touch you at the gallery.'

'How can you take that superior attitude with me,' she stormed, 'when you spent all your nights away from me at the cottage in the arms of your mistress?'

'If my art is my mistress,' he riposted, eyebrows mockingly high, 'then I spent every hour of every day and every night in her embrace.'

'That's not what I meant, and you know it! Why are you here? Did your lady-friend push you out of her bed now the exhibition's over?'

'This is where I live,' he answered levelly, getting to his feet. 'Isn't that a good enough reason? A man, like a woman, has a homing instinct.'

Now he was close to her again, she was overwhelmingly conscious of him, of his quizzical, uplifted brow; the way he towered over her; the midnight shadow around his stubborn jaw giving him a faintly devil-may-care look. It was dynamite to her senses. She wanted to fling herself at him and cry, 'Make love to me, darling, I can't live another minute without the feel of you against my flesh...'

The sardonic smile that slanted his mouth—as if he had guessed at her almost uncontrollable uprush of desire—acted like iced water on her inflamed feelings.

Her body began to shiver, letting her down.

Reaching for his jacket, he commanded softly, 'Come here.'

'No, thank you,' she replied, half turning, 'I'll——'

'I said *come here.*'

With half-reluctant, half-eager steps, she complied, feeling him turn her and slip the jacket over her shoulders. To her dismay, instead of ceasing, the shivering increased. He drew her down beside him on the sofa, taking her quivering form in his close, if coolly impersonal embrace.

Yet she was responding to him with every nerve in her body. The latent strength in those arms which created great masterpieces in stone and bronze made her head spin. The muscled fullness of his thighs was stirring in her a familiar, insistent desire. How often had those thighs enmeshed her limbs erotically between them, capturing her hips and waist and any other part of her they could encompass?

In sheer self-defence she eased away. Not for another moment could she endure being so close to him without giving herself away.

Leaning back, with narrowed gaze he swept her body, running his eyes over her breasts, penetrating the flimsy barrier of her nightdress, burning a river of fire over her from head to bare, clenched toes.

'You're too thin,' was his succinct, deliberately needling comment. 'Maybe Forrest prefers you that way? Unfortunately, I don't.'

The criticism, so unfair in the circumstances, caught her on the raw. She drew his jacket more securely around her, then immediately regretted the action. The musky male scent of his body, around which it had been wrapped, tantalised her, intensifying the pain she felt at his contemptuous attitude.

'So I don't attract you any more,' she hit back. 'Maybe it's better for both of us that I don't. As I saw a few hours ago, you don't belong to my world, nor I to yours.'

'As you never seem to tire of telling me.'

'Whereas,' she persisted, 'Johanna does belong. Isn't that lucky?'

'And Dave Forrest fits into your scheme of things very neatly. Well, he's the sort of guy who needs a prop, and what better physical and mental support could he find than you? Rest assured, Jemma,' he added, sarcasm curling his lips, 'you'll get the chance one day to marry a problem in your casebook. Which is what you thought you were taking on, wasn't it, when you married me?'

'I thought nothing of the sort!' she blurted out.

The tears behind her eyes were almost blinding her, the verbal knife he had just thrust into her making her bleed inside. I can't stand it any more, she told herself. If I don't get up and go now, the end of our marriage will come before daybreak.

'I'm going back to bed, Arne,' she said, rising unsteadily. 'This isn't getting us anywhere, is it?'

His only answer was to rise and pour himself another drink, standing with his back to her, his fingers clenched around the glass.

Gazing at him, Jemma thought she glimpsed a droop to the set of his shoulders. If only I could be sure, she thought, I'd go to him and put my arms around him, pull his head to my breast... She knew she was fooling herself. It wasn't her arms he wanted embracing him, it was Johanna's.

Dear God, she thought, lying sleeplessly on the bed, what can I do? I advise so many others, yet who can *I* turn to for help? I love him so, yet he has eyes and ears only for Johanna.

Wasn't it claimed that love broke down all barriers? There had to be a way, didn't there, to get through to him, to touch his warmth and humanity as she used to be able to do? To tear him from his new love, who was really his old love, and get him back?

It was like another self taking charge. For the second time that night she threw back the covers. Earlier, she had heard him come slowly up the stairs and close the door of the room along the landing.

This time, she reached for her wine velvet wrap, tying its belt. Then, before her courage deserted her, she half ran to the door of his room and threw it open. He lay on the bed partly covered by a towelling robe. His eyes opened wide at her sudden appearance, otherwise he remained still.

'Arne,' she heard herself saying, 'what are we going to do? About us? About everything?'

He stiffened, his brilliant blue eyes blazing to life. 'Do?' He looked her over, then slowly rose, his bare feet making damp imprints on the carpet. 'You want action?' He tugged at her belt and peeled the wrap from her shoulders. His hands ran over her slender form, then fitted under her armpits, making her sway towards him. 'So I'll deliver, my *darling* wife. Oh yes, I'll deliver. But the price will be high for the service I give—total amnesia where your current lover's concerned——'

'Will you listen to me?' she cried out, 'Dave's not my lover!' She paused, taking a chance with her next words. 'Any more than Tracey's your daughter.'

He released her, his eyes lifting from her body to her face. 'So you finally worked that one out. Very astute of you.'

'Only when I saw Dave and Tracey next to one another at the gallery this evening. Until then, I—I believed Johanna...'

He jerked her chin up. 'Did you really think so badly of my integrity you thought I'd lie to you about having a child by another woman—a child I didn't publicly acknowledge as my own?'

'I—it did occur to me, Arne, that you might just be protecting Dave——'

He threw her chin away. 'What the hell for? If she'd been mine, I'd have told the world, even if she had been born within another guy's marriage. What I told you about Johanna having a child by Dave Forrest—as a twisted kind of revenge against my not marrying her—was the truth.'

Jemma cursed herself for her lack of insight into this man's true character. And her failure to believe his explanation of the breaking up of his relationship with Johanna. 'Dave loves Tracey so much,' she said at last.

'So he should, since he fathered her. I love her, too. I love children in general. You know damned well how I feel about——'

'A family.' She stared at him. 'That baby I lost—*we* lost it, Arne. You and I. Yet *you* didn't believe *me* when I told you.'

He looked into her face for a long time, then his eyes narrowed angrily. 'My God,' he said at last, 'Johanna has a lot to answer for. But you can't deny the case against you seemed conclusive.'

'Circumstantial evidence each time,' Jemma admitted, 'and with Johanna's lies to back it up, almost impossible to disprove.' She added in a whisper, 'I was heartbroken, Arne, about losing the baby.'

'And you had to bear it alone.' A shaft of pain twisted his features.

She touched his hand. 'I wanted you to hold me, Arne, tell me you still loved me. That we could try again...'

He frowned as if unable to believe what she was implying. 'You've changed your mind? You want a child?'

'More than anything in the world. When I knew I was pregnant, I realised what a fool I'd been about my own inclinations. Any woman can have a career, but only you and I can give life and breath to our own offspring.'

He gripped her shoulders, his hold almost bruising. 'You're fully aware of what you're saying?'

With a tiny smile born of the seed of hope that had begun to grow inside her, she nodded. 'Sound in mind and body. Hand on my heart, I swear I want our baby, Arne. Any——' her voice wavered, 'any time you like. I'm—I'm at your disposal...'

He laughed at her statement. 'Are you, now? And suppose I said——'

That he still loved Johanna? He had said nothing to prove that he didn't. That was something she would have to accept. Maybe one day, when their child wound its magic around his heart, he might begin to love its mother, too.

'Suppose I said I wanted you here and now?'

She took a few quick breaths. 'Suppose you did, Arne?'

He made no move to follow words by action, so she searched his face, but it gave no clues to his thoughts. With small, impatient movements she pushed his robe from his shoulders and rested her cheek against his dark chest hair.

Still he did not stir, so she tugged at her nightgown, wriggling out of it until it fell to the floor. Then she put her body against his and placed swift kisses over his torso, putting out her tongue and licking his heated skin, using her teeth to nip, then throwing back her head in a kind of passionate defiance. If she was going to succeed in ousting Johanna from his affections—and she was— she had to use all the tricks she knew, and some she only guessed at, to achieve her object.

Looking into his face, she saw not the pleasure she had anticipated, but a suspicious frown. 'So who's been teaching you new tricks?' he grated.

His hands on her body had roughened and she shook her head fiercely. 'Not Dave. You have to stop believing there was ever anything between us. Dave's crazy about his wife. He's told me so often how much he loves her I've lost count. Even at the exhibition yesterday evening, he begged me to tell him how to get her back... Away from you——'

He cut off her words with his mouth, working at her lips with tongue and teeth until she parted them, allowing him access to the sweetly moist interior. Impelling her against his hard-boned nakedness, he ran his hand down her back until the swelling mound of her rear was in his keeping.

'She never had me,' he growled. 'She tried, my God, she tried, but in the end she got the message. That where she was concerned, I was, and for ever would be, unavailable.'

'But——' Jemma started to speak, unable to believe her ears, but his mouth cut off her words again.

Urging her closer still, his totally aroused state pressed into the heated softness of her flesh, bringing tiny cries into her throat. I'm like a starving creature, she thought dizzily, whimpering for food, but of the kind which only this man can give me.

The silky skin of her stomach quivered against his palms and she cried out his name as his searching fingertips found intimate, secret folds and valleys.

He impelled her backwards until her stumbling feet brought her against the bed. As she fell, he went with her, moving his mouth to find her breasts, teasing the swollen nipples with his tongue and drawing them between his lips, nipping them one after the other until she gasped for mercy.

'Please,' she said hoarsely, 'oh Arne, I want you so——'

'And my God,' he said hoarsely, 'I want you. I'm crazy for the feel of you beneath me, enclosing me. I want your body melting into mine, filling me, flowing round me with the blood in my veins...'

Such sweet endearments, such wonderful, loving words, she thought mistily. Yet, however much he might deny it, I know where his heart really is. He's turned the woman he loves most in the world into a work of art for all mankind to see...

He was possessing her now, and the singing joy of being joined to him again took away every other thought. Each step of the way she went with him, arching herself to accept his rhythmic movements, winding her limbs around him and crying out her love for him.

When she thought that even paradise itself could hold no greater joy, the pinnacle was reached and the very essence of him flowed into her. Her breaths came fast and she thought she would die of happiness.

As his head lay against her breasts, his breathing teased her tingling skin. She stroked his dark hair, running her palms over the muscles of his back and wondering how she had managed to live without him all those bitter, lonely weeks.

For a long time they lay entwined, then he moved, twisting her under him, and the lovemaking began all over again. Still Arne's desire persisted, and it wasn't until the grandfather clock struck five and the birds sang their brilliant songs of morning that, bodies still entwined, they slept deeply at last.

Stirring when the sun had risen high, she found that he was leaning over her, kissing her awake. A long sigh of contentment escaped her and she lay beside him, enfolded in his embrace. There was a small, troubled frown on her face as she ran her finger along his forehead and arched brows.

'Darling,' she murmured, 'wouldn't it be wonderful if the child we have inherits your artistic ability? Where my imagination should be there's an awful emptiness. I did tell you——'

His hand covered her lips. 'Tell me, lady, when your clients come to you with their problems and ask you to find answers, do you just stare at them blankly, or does your mind get to work visualising solutions—a better place for them to live, for instance, a new job for them, with better prospects? A happy ending to a marital split?'

'Yes, it does,' she answered, eyes bright with hope.

'You like winter trees against the sky?' he went on. 'The shape of leaves and flowers?'

Jemma nodded eagerly.

'Buds like beads on branches in spring?'

'Yes, yes I do.'

'Waterfalls, the shape of mountains?' Again she nodded. 'Well, that's all Nature's art.'

'But that's not art that comes from man,' she pointed out, tapping his head, 'from there, like yours.'

'What is man's art if not taken from Nature? That's an artist's chief source, springboard, inspiration, call it what you like, that's where it ultimately comes from. What's more, *you* can see it, too. So where's this mind barrier you keep claiming divides us?'

He pulled her even closer.

'You mean it doesn't exist?' she asked delightedly.

'It doesn't exist. Take it from me, my darling counsellor,' he smiled into her eyes, 'you've got imagination, and most certainly artistic appreciation, in addition to all your other fantastic qualities.'

'Darling,' she rubbed her forehead against him, 'thanks for that wonderful encouragement.' And, she thought happily, for giving me the key to that secret part of your life I've wanted for so long to share.

'Any time,' he joked, then, with an exasperated sigh, pulled her the length of him. 'Oh, Jemma, Jemma,' he muttered, his lips against her throat, 'have you any idea what you've been doing to me these past weeks? Killing me with a thousand cuts...' His teeth played a little angrily with her ear lobe.

Filled with happiness though she was, she could not let him get away with that. 'No, no, Arne. It's what *you've* been doing to me! Living with Johanna, painting her, sculpting her, making love to her...'

He lifted himself above her, his eyes pinpoints of blinding light. 'What the hell are you talking about? I told you she got nowhere with me. To put it bluntly, even posing naked she had no effect whatever on my reflexes.'

Jemma frowned uncertainly. 'Are you sure you don't still love her? You see, she told me about that sculpture.'

He rolled away from her. 'Told you what about the sculpture?' His eyes were cooler now, making her shiver. 'I'm surprised it interested you. You seemed completely indifferent to it. You left the gallery a couple of minutes before the unveiling.'

'What did you expect me to do,' she cried, dismayed that the chasm was opening up between them again, 'stay there and watch as the face of the woman you loved above any other was shown to the world.'

His eyes narrowed. 'Yes, I did. So why didn't you?'

She stared at him in disbelief. 'Surely you can imagine how I felt? It would have been hell watching Johanna's face unveiled as that of the woman you——'

'*Johanna's face?*' His lips curled into a thin angry line.

'Who else's?' she asked, mystified. 'Johanna told me she'd seen it——'

'No one has seen it, except me. It has been in a locked studio, and covered throughout its entire existence, until its unveiling at the show.'

'You mean Johanna——?' Jemma remembered then that Johanna had not actually said that the face in the sculpture was hers. But there was no doubt at all that she implied it.

'I mean Johanna twisted the truth again. She had this idea fixed in her head that although I'd thrown her out of my life a few years ago, I still loved her. Let me tell you something, Jemma.' He rested on his elbow and turned her to face him. 'It wasn't only because she refused to have a child if we'd married. After all, I married you, although you'd made it plain you wanted to wait before having one. The simple truth is that I just didn't love her enough.'

His passionate gaze raked the glowing, naked body before him and he smiled. 'Then, my living, loving Venus,' he went on, 'as I said, after meeting you I realised that whatever I had felt for her in the past, it had never been love.'

He swung from the bed. 'Join me in the shower, then get dressed. We're going places, you and I.'

Outside the Oceanic Gallery, the security man was helping three people into a taxi. As it cruised slowly from the kerb, the window was lowered and a man's voice shouted. Arne, handing over the keys of his car for parking, looked up.

'Hey, you two!' Dave saluted, then gave the thumbs up sign.

Jemma had never seen him so happy. On his lap was a smiling Tracey, while at his side sat his wife whose eyes, as she turned to wave from the rear window, had never shone brighter.

One marriage, Jemma thought delightedly, saved from the rocks.

Early though it was, people were milling around the gallery. Seizing Jemma's hand, Arne pulled her behind him. At the end of the high-ceilinged room, in pride of place, worked in glowing bronze, stood the great work of art. Its title was displayed under lights. 'Man, Woman and Child', it announced. But there was no child.

Jemma, her hand firmly in Arne's grip, searched for it. Then the significance of the sculpture hit her, its symbolism making such an impact, she swayed.

The man portrayed, his body flowing with muscle, strength and power, supported the unclothed body of a woman, while the other arm, its hand grown huge, the back of it being assaulted by man-made weapons of destruction, was held over the woman's enlarged stomach.

The great hand was raised high, *protecting the unborn child . . . protecting the future of mankind . . .*

On the man's face—bearing a marked similarity to Arne's—was a look of fierce determination, yet of infinite gentleness, while the woman's—*the woman's face was hers!*

Gasping, she lifted her eyes to his. 'Arne, the woman, she's——?'

'You. Who else? The woman I love most in the world. Didn't you know? How many times,' his eyes burned with love and passion, 'do I have to tell you? To *show* you?'

'Mrs Power?'

Jemma hesitated, then turned. The man who had spoken stood behind her, holding a camera. 'I see the resemblance now,' the photographer said. 'The woman in the sculpture, sir, is your wife?'

Another man, notebook in hand, joined him. 'Press,' he announced, displaying his card.

'You don't say,' commented Arne drily.

'A picture, sir, madam?' The photographer took one before gaining their permission. 'Just one more. Thanks a lot. It's not often we get a story like this.'

Arne threw back his head in laughter. 'Is it such a rarity these days that a husband loves his wife so much he wants to tell the world?'

'"Mrs Power"?' was all Jemma, bewildered and smiling, could say. 'You've got the wrong name. I'm Mrs Arne Drummond, aren't I, darling?'

She wound her arms round Arne's neck and lifted up her face for his kiss. The one she received was lingering and ardent. The cameras—there were three more now—clicked madly.

Arne smiled into her eyes. 'You're also Mrs Armin Power, my love. Never forget that.'

She gazed up at him, laughing. 'Would you really expect a woman—any woman—ever to forget that she was married to two men at once? And,' she expelled a happy, sighing breath, 'what men!'

Mills & Boon

AND THEN HE KISSED HER...

This is the title of our new venture — an audio tape designed to help you become a successful Mills & Boon author!

In the past, those of you who asked us for advice on how to write for Mills & Boon have been supplied with brief printed guidelines. Our new tape expands on these and, by carefully chosen examples, shows you how to make your story come alive. And we think you'll enjoy listening to it.

You can still get the printed guidelines by writing to our Editorial Department. But, if you would like to have the tape, please send a cheque or postal order for £4.95 (which includes VAT and postage) to:

VAT REG. No. 232 4334 96

- -

AND THEN HE KISSED HER...

To: Mills & Boon Reader Service, FREEPOST, P.O. Box 236, Croydon, Surrey CR9 9EL.

Please send me _____ copies of the audio tape. I enclose a cheque/postal order*, crossed and made payable to Mills & Boon Reader Service, for the sum of £_____ . *Please delete whichever is not applicable.

Signature _____

Name (BLOCK LETTERS) _____

Address _____

_____ Post Code _____

YOU MAY BE MAILED WITH OTHER OFFERS AS A RESULT OF THIS APPLICATION   ED1

Mills & Boon present
the 75th Romance of one of their top authors

CHARLOTTE LAMB
NO MORE
LONELY NIGHTS

Charlotte Lamb's popularity speaks for itself. This intriguing and romantic story, tying together the hard high powered world of the business magnate with the softness of the human heart, is destined to become a collector's item.

Not to buy this title is to miss a classic.

Published: September 1988   Price £1.50

Available from Boots, Martins, John Menzies, W.H. Smith, Woolworths and other paperback stockists.

2 NEW
W⬤RLDWIDE
TITLES FOR SEPTEMBER

The tough male environment of the New Orlean's Police Department . . .
The arrival of an attractive new female psychologist . . .
The obsessive behaviour of one officer with his career at stake . . .
After Midnight is the compelling story of a woman striving to succeed in a man's world.

£2.50

Hardship turns to success in Evan and Amanda's marriage — until tragedy drives them apart.

3 years later, as Amanda is about to re-marry, Evan re-appears with plans to change her mind.

Realism and emotional tension run high in Marisa Carroll's latest novel *Remembered Magic.*

£2.25

From Boots, Martins, John Menzies, W H Smith, Woolworth and other paperback stockists.

SPOT THE COUPLE
AND WIN A
£1,000
REAL PEARL NECKLACE
PLUS 10 PAIRS OF REAL PEARL EAR STUDS WORTH OVER £100 EACH

A

B

No piece of jewellery is more romantic than the soft glow and lustre of a real pearl necklace, pearls that grow mysteriously from a grain of sand to a jewel that has a romantic history that can be traced back to Cleopatra and beyond.

To enter just study Photograph A showing a young couple. Then look carefully at Photograph B showing the same section of the river. Decide where you think the couple are standing and mark their position with a cross in pen.

Complete the entry form below and mail your entry PLUS TWO OTHER "SPOT THE COUPLE" Competition Pages from June, July or August Mills and Boon paperbacks, to Spot the Couple, Mills and Boon Limited, Eton House, 18/24 Paradise Road, Richmond, Surrey, TW9 1SR, England. All entries must be received by December 31st 1988.

RULES

1. This competition is open to all Mills & Boon readers with the exception of those living in countries where such a promotion is illegal and employees of Mills & Boon Limited, their agents, anyone else directly connected with the competition and their families.
2. This competition applies only to books purchased outside the U.K. and Eire.
3. All entries must be received by December 31st 1988.
4. The first prize will be awarded to the competitor who most nearly identifies the position of the couple as determined by a panel of judges. Runner-up prizes will be awarded to the next ten most accurate entries.
5. Competitors may enter as often as they wish as long as each entry is accompanied by two additional proofs of purchase. Only one prize per household is permitted.
6. Winners will be notified during February 1989 and a list of winners may be obtained by sending a stamped addressed envelope marked "Winners" to the competition address.
7. Responsibility cannot be accepted for entries lost, damaged or delayed in transit. Illegible or altered entries will be disqualified.

ENTRY FORM

Name _____

Address _____

_____

I bought this book in TOWN _____ COUNTRY _____

This offer applies only to books purchased outside the UK & Eire.
You may be mailed with other offers as a result of this application.